TEACHING BY HAND

LEARNING BY HEART

Bruce Fertman started his studies with the Alexander Technique in 1973. He studied regularly with Marjorie Barstow 1975-88, and started teaching the Alexander Technique in 1976. His teaching embodies a lifetime of movement training, having trained in gymnastics, modern dance, ballet contact improvisation, tai chi chu'an, aikido, chanoyu, Argentine tango, and kyudo. He co-founded the Alexander Alliance International in 1982, and since 1987 has been teaching annually in the US, Europe and Asia. Currently he directs the Alexander Alliance Germany and is a senior teacher for Alexander Alliance schools in Japan, the U.S. and South Korea. He also runs postgraduate training programmes in England and Switzerland.

In gratitude to
Rebbe Zalman Schachter-Shalomi
Marjorie L. Barstow
Byron Katie

Bruce Fertman

TEACHING BY HAND
LEARNING BY HEART

Delving into the Work of F. M. Alexander

Mouritz

First published February 2018 by

Mouritz
6 Ravenslea Road
London SW12 8SB
United Kingdom

Some names and identifying details have been
changed to protect the privacy of individuals.

ISBN 978-0-9954911-5-1 Paperback
A CIP Catalogue record for this book
is available from the British Library

Layout and typesetting
by Jean M. O. Fischer

Set in Cardo and Sabon in Adobe Indesign

Printed on 80gsm Opaque
by Imprint Digital, Devon, United Kingdom

CONTENTS

FOREWORD

Once I asked a man what he did for a living and he said, 'I'm an anesthesiologist. And you?' he asked. 'I'm an esthesiologist. You say to people, you're not going to feel a thing, and I say to people, you are about to feel everything.'

Rather than becoming a physician, I became a metaphysician, not in the academic sense, though I did bumble through as an undergraduate philosophy major studying primarily western European philosophy, my favourite characters being Heraclitus, Socrates, Spinoza, Schopenhauer, Heidegger, Nietzsche, William James, Emerson, and Martin Buber.

I'm a practising metaphysician, a metaphysician by trade. I attend to people's subjective sense of time and space, to their felt experience of being and becoming.

If we were only physical we would have no need for the words mind, heart, and soul. We can physically reduce ourselves down to oxygen, carbon, hydrogen, nitrogen, calcium, phosphorus, etc., but we don't go around feeling like oxygen, carbon, hydrogen, nitrogen, calcium and phosphorus. That's not our experience of who we are. That's what we are.

When I first started out as an Alexander teacher I was a movement artist and educator. My mentor, Marjorie ('Marj') Barstow, was too. She used to talk about life as movement. She'd say in her spare, enigmatic way, 'It's all about movement.'

Yes, life comes to pass, not to stay. Even after we die our bodies, via decomposition, keep moving. But I think many of us who studied with Marj, especially those of us who were athletes, dancers, and martial artists, interpreted that statement more narrowly. The work became to a large degree about human movement potential, about the quality of our coordination, about physical freedom and ease.

For 25 years Richard M. Gummere Jr. ('Buzz'), a friend of Marjorie Barstow, served as historian and philosophic advisor for the Alexander Alliance, a community/school dedicated to the training of Alexander teachers founded in 1982 by Martha Hansen Fertman and me. Buzz studied briefly with John Dewey. He trained with F. M. Alexander, A. R. Alexander, and Marjorie Barstow. He trained alongside Frank Pierce Jones. Buzz was exceptionally intelligent. He could finish the *New York Times* Sunday crossword puzzle faster than any man alive. Buzz taught Greek and Latin. He helped found Hampshire College, was the Dean at Bard College, and a career counselor at Columbia University. Why he and his wife, Peg Gummere, drove down from Woodstock, New York, almost every month, year after year, to the Alexander Alliance I do not know. I do know Buzz loved our community, and my kids, and we loved him. And we learned from him, continually. Maybe that's why.

After one of my classes Buzz came up to me and complimented me on my class. 'You really got everyone organized and moving so well. You're a great movement teacher.' That should have felt like a compliment, but it didn't. Why didn't Buzz say I was a great Alexander teacher? Like Socrates, Buzz had his way of throwing me into a state of constructive doubt.

At the end of a retreat we were saying our goodbyes and I asked Buzz, as I did often, 'Do you have any suggestions for me, something you'd like me to consider?' He looked at me for a moment, quite sternly, and said, 'What's the difference between a movement teacher and an Alexander teacher?' Then he smiled and laughed and thanked me, as he always did.

It's taken me 30 years to live into the answer to that question. As a movement teacher my work revolved around improving a person's level of functional and structural integration, around boosting efficiency and effectiveness in whatever a person chooses to do, be it hammering a nail, walking down the street, playing volley ball, or singing an aria.

Now my work as an Alexander teacher revolves around how we choose to respond to the world within us and all around us. How do we choose to respond to our own thoughts and emotions, to physical sensations both pleasant and unpleasant? How do we choose to respond to criticism, to praise, to deadlines, to the wind? How do we best adapt to an ever-changing world, to our uncertain futures? The question is not how can we move well, but how can we move well through the course of our lives, how can we live life fluidly, articulately, powerfully, sensitively, pleasurably, and responsibly?

It's taken time, not years, but decades for me to make my way from being a movement teacher to becoming an Alexander teacher. It's been a long road, a path, a way of walking through the world. For many years I walked alongside my teachers. They grew old and died before getting to the end of the road. This road is longer than any one person's life.

While walking there are times when, suddenly, I am compelled to sit down and write, so I do. Ever since I left my parents' home, writing has been for me a need, something I did and still do to sort out my own thoughts, to give shape to my ideas, to remember what I have to do each day.

Living my life as an Alexander teacher has been and remains a privilege and a delight. Not many Alexander teachers manage to carve out a good living. It's possible but it requires additional knowledge and skills other than a deep understanding of Alexander's work and the ability to communicate that understanding to others. Somehow we have to know how to present who we are, the wisdom we embody, and the love in our hearts.

It is as if we have to make a documentary about our work as we are living our work. No small task, but a potentially enjoyable and clarifying one. It has been for me.

Documenting my work, and by my work I mean Alexander's work as interpreted and expressed through me, is for me an act of love. It's like falling madly in love with someone and finding yourself writing love letters to them, every day. You search for the right words, beautiful words. You want to gaze at them, photograph them, you want to think about them, you want to touch them. You want to express your love for them to the whole world.

I have been in love with Alexander's work for 47 years. Soon we will have our fiftieth wedding anniversary. Not only have I collected and saved my love letters, some of which I share with you here, but I've also collected stories, lots of stories, and photos too.

Photography has been my way of capturing the visual beauty of the work. For years I watched Marjorie Barstow open one person after another, revealing their inner beauty, their humanity, their inherent dignity. Seeing this luminous transparency, seeing the halo within every human being often moved me to tears. It is what made me decide to become an Alexander teacher. I share some of these images with you here as well.

For some of you this book will serve as an introduction to Alexander's work. May it lead you to teachers who will accompany you, for a precious while, along your way.

For those of you who have found your teachers, this book may motivate you to take the work ever more to heart, to delve into the depth and breadth of the work.

And for those of you who are Alexander trainees and fellow teachers, may this book embolden you to take the work beyond the body into the realm of being, and beyond movement into the world of meaning.

May this book remind you of all that is worth loving inside the work of F. M. Alexander.

HE WHO SINGS A LASTING SONG – INTRODUCING F. M. ALEXANDER'S WORK

To be good at introducing Alexander's work it is necessary to be excited and in love with his work. But there is more. We've got to be living the work every day, continually experimenting with its foundational ideas and principles, and finding contemporary, understandable language for those ideas and principles. We've got to be able to give voice to kinaesthetic and proprioceptive experience. And if we want Alexander's work to be not only about the body and movement but about living, we've also got to know how to think metaphorically about the body and movement.

Over the years I have created many of what I call movement metaphors. A movement metaphor is some action a person does, or a group of people do, that conveys through movement a universal principle, conveys a universal principle not only intellectually but physically. It is one thing to understand a truth; it is another thing to embody a truth. In 'A Prayer for Old Age', W. B. Yeats writes:

God guard me from those thoughts men think
In the mind alone;
He that sings a lasting song
Thinks in a marrow-bone.

A movement metaphor leads to an experienced truth, a felt truth known in a marrow-bone. John Dewey, the American philosopher and educator, and a long-term student of the Alexander Technique wrote, 'My theories of mind-body required contact with the work of F. M. Alexander, and in later years his brother A. R., to transform them into realities.' That is, Dewey understood the idea of mind-body unity in the mind alone, but later, through Alexander's work, came to understand the idea of mind-body unity in his marrow-bone. He became able to embody the idea, to live the idea. It was no longer a theory. It had become a practice.

Here is a movement metaphor I often use when introducing Alexander's work.

'Would you like to know, and more importantly, experience, in ten minutes, the foundational principle underlying Alexander's work?' I say to a group of new students.

Looking around I see some skeptical smiles and hear a little laughter. 'Well, would you?' I see many heads nodding.

'Okay, everyone stand up.' I gather together about nine chairs, and with them I make a little circle, leaving about a five-foot opening. There are 20 students in the room.

'Okay, imagine we're in Tokyo. It's 8:30 in the morning and we've all got to be at work by 9:00. Let's make two lines, one on either side of the doors. In about two minutes the train is going to pull up right on time. As always, the doors will open, people will come flooding out like water through an opened dam. When they are finally all out, we will enter the train, trying to be polite, but also trying to get into the train because there are more people outside the train waiting to get into the train than can fit into the train. After all of you get in a little man with white gloves (that will be me) will push all of you further into the train, packing you in like sardines in a tin can so a few more people can get in. Then the doors will close and the train will leave. Here comes the train, right on time.'

'Wait, wait. Let all the people come out.' After about 30 seconds I say, 'Okay. Go ahead in.' The students crowd in like a herd of cows. Not everyone can fit. I gently but firmly push the remaining three students into the subway car. I close off the opening with three chairs and manage to squeeze myself into the car.

'Okay. No one move. Stay exactly how you are, as if I've just pushed the pause button. Sense how you feel, beginning down at your feet, and slowly work up until you get to the top of your head. Don't leave out any part of you. And don't move or change anything.

'Keep holding yourself as you are and succinctly and specifically tell me what is going on, from the bottom up.'

'Feet?'

There's no space between my feet.

'Legs?'

My knees are locked and my thighs are tight.

'Pelvis?'

I'm squeezing my butt.

'Torso?'

I'm pushing my chest in.

'Shoulders?'

My shoulders are up by my ears.

'Arms?'

My arms are pressing against the sides of my body.

'Hands?'

My fingers are interlaced and tightly locked together.

'Is anyone breathing?' Laughter.

'Don't move. Keep holding yourself as you are.'

'Neck and head?'

I'm holding my neck and head very still. It's frozen stiff.
My head is pushing down into my neck.
'Jaw?'
I'm clenching my jaw.
'Teeth?'
My teeth are pressing against each other.
'Tongue?'
My tongue is pushing against the roof of my mouth.
'Eyes?'
My eyes are cast down and I'm not seeing anything.
'One by one, follow my instructions.

'Put a tiny bit of space between your feet, as much as you can without intruding into anyone's space.

'Release the tension in your legs and belly and let yourself breathe.

'Let your shoulders spread apart and let your arms rest at your sides. If they touch someone, figure out where you can put them without putting effort into your arms or hands.

'Continue breathing and relax your jaw, teeth, and tongue.'

The whole room seems to inhale at once.

'Let your eyes look out and around. Look up and see all the space above your heads.

'What do you notice?'

It's weird. I'm taking up more room and at the same time I feel like there is more space around me and not less. That doesn't make sense.

'I know. I don't understand it either, but this is what happens whenever I do this with a group of people, or when I do it by myself for real in Tokyo or Osaka at 8:30 in the morning. Okay, the train is slowing down. We are approaching our stop. The train will stop. The doors will open. You will exit the train.' I move the three chairs away. Everyone leaves the 'train'.

'Alright, everyone, let's sit down where we are. I want to ask you a question. What made you tense?'

The lack of space.

All the people.

The lack of time.

'Any other possibilities?'

I made myself tense.

'Well, isn't it true? Who tightened all those muscles? Did the person next to you do that to you?'

I can see some light bulbs going off.

Yes, I could feel it. Nothing out there made me tense. I did it entirely by myself. That's amazing.

'Yes it is, and it is great news. If we are the person tying ourselves up in a knot, then we are the person who can untie the knot. If someone else has tied us up, then we become victims, and we have to wait for them or for someone to untie us. That is bad news.

'Imagine this. It's true. Viktor Frankl was Professor of Neurology and Psychiatry at the Universtity of Vienna Medical School. For three years he lived in concentration camps during World War II, in Theresienstadt, Auschwitz, and Dachau. One day he had a revelation and at that moment he became a free man. He writes in *Man's Search For Meaning*, "The one thing you can't take away from me is the way I choose to respond to what you do to me. The last of one's freedoms is to choose one's attitude in any given circumstance." '

The room is quiet, very quiet.

'Okay. Let's do it again. Everything is going to happen the way it happened before, like in the movie, *Groundhog Day*, one of my all-time favourite movies, except one thing will be different.

'So, we're in Tokyo. It's 8:30 in the morning, and we've all got to be at work by 9:00. We make two lines, one on either side of the doors. In about two minutes, the train is going to pull up. The doors will open, people will leave the train. It will take about 30 seconds. When they are finally all out, we will enter the train, trying to be polite, but also trying to get into the train because there are more people out of the train waiting to get into the train than can fit into the train. After all of you get in, the little man with white gloves will push all of you further into the train. Then the doors will close, and the train will leave.

'But this time, before you get into the train, you will make a decision. You will decide how you want to be, how you want to respond to your circumstances. You know from experience that no one can tie you up in a knot except you. No one. No thing. Ever. Ask yourself, "Is there any real reason why I have to put my feet together, make my legs rigid, hold my breath, press my chest in, lift my shoulders, press my arms against my sides, lock my fingers together, tighten my neck, clench my jaw and teeth, or press my tongue against the roof of my mouth? Is there any reason why I have to look down?"

'Make your decision not to do what you don't want to do. And decide to stick to your decision no matter what happens, no matter how strange it feels. The train is coming. Have you made your decision?'

The people leave the 'train'. Everyone enters the 'train'. After gently pushing everyone in I enter and close the circle. 'How is everyone doing?'

I'm fine. I feel good.

There's a lot more room in here than before.

I am actually enjoying the people around me. I feel protected by them. I feel friendly. I feel safe.

'Okay. We are arriving at our station. The doors will open and off you will go to work.' I remove the three chairs and everyone leaves the train. There's a softness in the air.

'Let's sit down. There it is, the foundational principle underlying Alexander's work. What is it?'

We're free.

We have choice.

'Did you feel it? Do you know that it's true? If we are wide awake, here and now, we can choose how we want to respond to what is happening around us and within us. It takes practice. That's the truth that Alexander stumbled into and spent his entire life investigating and attempting to impart to others.'

A movement metaphor. Using movement to arrive at meaning. Using the physical to experience the metaphysical.

I could have just explained this idea to the group and quoted Viktor Frankl, but had I not led the group through this movement metaphor they would not have felt the truth behind this principle. It's through the physicalizing of the principle that the principle becomes a reality. The physicalizing of philosophy, or what I call 'somasophy', a body of knowledge, or body wisdom.

But there is more. If we are to be able to teach Alexander's work within a group setting, we need to know how to teach people to see themselves and others benevolently and accurately. We've got to get our students lovingly seeing how we humans do what we do, and precisely how we interfere with what we do. We've not only got to know how to make the unconscious conscious, we've got to know how to make the invisible visible.

We need to be able to see – and get our students to see – postural, tensional, and motional patterns. But we also need to be able to see, and get our students to see, learning patterns, interactional patterns, vocal patterns, gestural patterns, breathing patterns, and persona patterns.

And more. We need hands capable of bringing about not only dramatic experiences of kinaesthetic lightness, but also surprising experiences of integration, experiences of being at once soft and strong, light and substantial, relaxed and ready, stable and mobile, unified and articulate, gathered and expansive, open and focused, spontaneous and deliberate, committed and free.

Many young, less experienced Alexander teachers feel intimidated teaching the work in groups. It can be unnerving having people watch you as you work. It helps to know structures through which you can disclose the work, step by step, layer by layer, one idea at a time, one experience at a time.

Whether you are a student or a teacher of Alexander's work, I invite you to take several introductory workshops with me. Right now. I invite you to walk alongside me, down the road I have been walking down for 47 years, down the same road walked by my teachers before me.

We will enter Alexander's work through eight different doors, through sport, nature, anatomy, sensory life, social biology, theology, mysticism, and art.

Part One

THE WORK AT HAND

To receive everything, one must open one's hands and give.

Taisen Deshimaru

1 THE WAY OF IT

In Japan, in a hospital, I am with a group of young physical therapists. The head of the physical therapy department, having taken a workshop with me several months earlier, realized two key elements missing in the training of physical therapists. Yes, they learned a lot of specific techniques for lots of specific problems. They learned about different approaches to physical therapy, mostly theory. But what they were not being taught was how to use their hands sensitively, nor were they being taught how to use their bodies well as they worked, often for twelve hours a day, six days a week. Why this glaring omission? Why not a class in 'Touch for Physical Therapists', or 'Movement for Physical Therapists'? The department head decided it was time to do something about this.

INTEGRATION

'The Alexander Technique is not a technique, not in the same way you guys learn techniques for working with adhesive capsulitis (frozen shoulder, or in Japan it is known as the '50-year-old shoulder'), or hemiplegia (severe strokes), or dysphagia (swallowing disorders). The Alexander Technique is not a technique for anything particular.

'The Alexander Technique is an inquiry into human integration, into what integration is, what restores it, and what disturbs it.

It's a foundational study. Integration underlies everything we do. The more of it we have, the easier it is to do what we're doing.

'So what is integration? Physical therapists help people a lot with strength, flexibility, and coordination, very important work. Integration includes all of these but is, at the same time, something distinct from them. For example, a baby can scream holy hell for an hour and not lose its voice. Why is that? Why can't a grown up do that? A baby will reach for something, but never over-reach for something. They will only extend their arms so far and no farther. Why is that? Babies will work for a long time figuring out how to pick up a pea on their plate, but will never distort their hands or bodies while they're doing it. They just won't distort themselves. They are somehow prewired, preprogrammed to remain whole, all of a piece, a flexible unit. That's integration.'

'So why do we lose it? I don't know. How do we lose it? I don't know that either, but I've got a few theories. What I observe is that in the process of our becoming coordinated something happens. At some point we've got to learn how to button our shirt, tie our shoes, eat with *hashi* (chopsticks). We've got to learn how to speak, how to ride a bicycle, how to write *hiragana*. Did you ever see little kids trying to write *hiragana*? There it is. Children disintegrating. Their tongues are sticking out of the corners of their mouths, they're not breathing, their heads are hanging down, spines bent and twisted, little hands gripping their pencils for dear life. And the more pressure around learning, the more felt fear, the more the body falls apart. There's no preventing it entirely, no matter how great your parents are, or your teachers, or your culture. Sooner or later it's going to happen to everyone, more or less. The fall from grace. Somehow, we've got to find our way back to the garden.'

BULLDOGGING

'Have you ever been to a rodeo? I haven't, but in New Mexico, where I happen to live half the year, you might walk into a bar, look up at a TV and see one. A rodeo's a contest where cowboys and cowgirls show their skill at riding broncos, roping calves, and wrestling steers. These are for the most part practical skills ranchers need in order to round up cattle, count them, or brand them.

Fig. 2.

'Legend has it Marjorie Barstow, one of the first people certified to teach the Alexander Technique, and my mentor of 16 years, took Frank Pierce Jones, an Alexander teacher but also a classics professor at Brown University, an East Coast intellectual, a man who would never find himself at a rodeo, except for on this day, when Marj wanted to show him what the Alexander Technique was all about.

'"Frank, in a minute a big, mean steer is going to explode out of that gate, and out of the gate next to it a cowboy on a horse is going to burst out, and that cowboy is going to do his best to lean over, grab that steer's horns, dig his heels into the dirt, and take that steer down. And that steer is going to do his best not to let him."

'The gates open. Frank watches. He sees the cowboy lean over, take the horns, snap them back, jam the back of the steers' skull into his massive neck while twisting that neck to the side. The steer, unable to stay on his legs, finally falls, crashing to the ground.

'"What did you see Frank?" "Not too much," Frank says. "Keep watching Frank." They watched, and as they watched, little by little Marj got Frank to see exactly what was happening. "You see Frank, the cowboy snaps the steer's head back, and jams it into his neck. That compresses the steer's entire spine. Now the steer can't breathe. His front legs begin to buckle. His pelvis tilts under. His hind legs can't get any traction. That steer's got nothing left."

'There's one last cowboy to go. Looking down at him as he sits on his horse, Frank can see that this cowboy doesn't look well. He's slouched back in the saddle; the horse's head is dropped way down. Maybe the cowboy was out late. Maybe he drank more than he should have. The gates swing open, the steer gets the jump on him; the cowboy catches up, leans over, grabs the horns but can't seem to snap the head back. Rather than the horns going back, Frank sees them rotating slightly forward, the neck looks enormous, the steer's ribs are widening as air fills his huge lungs. The steer's body seems to be getting longer, his front legs are dropping powerfully right under his body, his pelvis is high and out, his tail is up, his haunches look enormous. His back hooves are driving him forward like a train. Meanwhile, the cowboy looks like a flag flapping in the wind.

"Now that's the way of it," Marj says. "That's how it works, that's what we're after. We've got that kind of organized power in us too. We're just interfering with it all the time. That's what Alexander figured out.'"

The young physical therapists looked tired at the beginning of the workshop, but now they were wide awake.

'And that's what I mean when I use the word integration. I mean that naturally organized power and freedom in all of us.

'Okay, enough sitting. Why don't you stand up?' The second they start to stand up I tell them to stop and just stay where they are.

'Don't move a muscle. Where are your horns, I mean, if you had horns? Are they rotating forward or are they rotating backwards?' My eyes see one guy whose head is really jammed into his neck. I walk over and kneel down on one knee in front of him. I invite everyone to come closer so they can see us. I scoop his head lightly into my hands, the way my grandmother would do to me when she greeted me, and I gently tilt his imaginary horns forward. His spine surges up. Everyone can see the power filling his body. 'That's the steer,' I say, 'that's the bull.'

I guide his weight over his sitbones, then over his feet, and without any effort, he rises to a stand. 'How was that,' I ask? Smiling, dazed, he says, '*Zen zen chigau!* Totally different! I floated onto my feet.' 'Well,' I say, 'that's what happens when the cowboy is off your back.

'Here's where it gets interesting. We've all got a steer inside of us. I call that your mammal body. And we all have a cowboy inside of us. That's your acquired body, or what I sometimes call your cultural body. And sometimes our acquired body, our cultural body, works against our mammal body, our natural body. There's a conflict in there. We're fighting against ourselves. And it can get dangerous. The steer can get hurt, and the cowboy too.

'Now, our cowboy can't take us down by our horns because we don't have horns, and besides, the cowboy is not outside of us. So how does the cowboy within us bring us down? Well, instead of coming at us from on top of our heads, he comes at us from below our heads, from our necks. It's like he's hiding there inside our neck, looking up, reaching up, and pulling our skull back and pressing it down into our spines. That's not the only place where he hangs out, but it's definitely one of his favourite places from which to operate. It is because the cowboy knows a universal principle of movement: where the head goes, the body follows.

'Here's what's very cool. Our mammal body has got a lot of energy in it. And our cowboy body does too. Now, if they're going at each other, if they're using up all of our energy fighting with each other, then we don't have the energy we need to get on with our lives. If we can get the energy of the mammal body and the energy of the cowboy body to harmonize, to join together toward a common purpose, if we can get them both working for us, then just imagine how much energy that would free up.

'That's why it felt so effortless standing up. Not only was the cowboy off your back, the cowboy was actually helping you get up! So you're going from having almost no available energy to stand up, to having a surplus of energy to stand up. Now, that's exciting. Imagine what it would feel like to work with patients with all that organized energy, what it would be like to move through your day like that.'

Over the next half hour, I do this with about ten students. I make a point of always catching a person unaware that their horns are pulling back. 'Don't move,' I tell her. 'You're perfect just like that. Okay, I'm going to be the cowboy.' I place my hands around her head, but this time I put a slight pressure with my little fingers against the back of her neck, and take her more into her 'disintegration pattern', gently getting her throat to bulge forward, which immediately tilts her head back, collapses her chest, and tucks her pelvis under.

'Now, I'm going to replace the cowboy within you with the Alexander teacher within you.' Finding the potential spring in her spine, I guide her back into her 'integration pattern.'

'Let me ask all of you. Who is your cowboy? When is your cowboy really taking you down? When is your disintegration pattern strongest, not just as a physical therapist, but as a person?'

The room gets very quiet. Finally someone speaks.

After a twelve-hour shift I've got one more patient and then paper work to do. I'm exhausted and totally collapsed.

When my mother calls me up and complains to me about my sister and how she pressures her kids all the time and never lets them play, I find myself curling over and all I want to do is get off the phone.

When I get home from work and my husband wants me to cook a good dinner and I don't want to cook, but I do it anyway. So I move as quickly as I can, but I can feel how much my body wants to lie down. It's really hard.

'Yes, when the bull is tired, the cowboy can really bring us down. That's when it helps to know how to get the cowboy to work for us and not against us. It's learnable.

'Now, I've got about seven younger Alexander teachers in the room with me.' Just as I watched my mentor, Marj Barstow, give scores of introductory workshops, now my students come to learn and assist me. 'Okay, teachers in the room, it's time to give everyone this experience!' I can sense a bit of panic in the air. I know what they're afraid of. 'Don't be afraid of taking people down,' I say to them. 'Do it. It's good for them. It's good for everyone. We want to stimulate spring in the spine. When you buckle a person's neck forward and press their head gently into their spine, it's an intelligent response for the body to go into a collapse pattern. If the spine is too rigid and can't do that, there's a problem. So take people down, softly, and get them to know what's happening down there. Lead them down in a way that makes their spines springy. Load the spring. Fill it with potential energy. Then take the pressure off it and let it spring back up. Get to work. Have fun.'

By the end of the first morning we are off to a good start. Everyone's got a clear idea of what Alexander's work is about. They're beginning to see what the cowboy within feels like, and what the steer within feels like. They've all felt the power of their mammal body when the cowboy is working for it, and the weakness of the mammal body when the cowboy is working against it.

Their Own Story

I want to tell them about their own country's story of the ox and the ox herder, known as the Zen Oxherd Pictures. About the boy who finds the wild ox and tries to tame it, how he has a real hard time of it, and how both he and the ox end up exhausted. I want to tell them how, if they just hang in there, and study for years, the ox and the ox herder will come to trust one another, and they'll begin to work together. The fighting will stop. But I decide not to go there.

'Have a good lunch. Get some fresh air. Move around. Rest a bit. Come back ready to work.'

'*Doumo arigatou gosaimashita*, thank you very much,' I say, bowing, grateful after all these years still to be teaching, grateful there are young people out there interested in what I know. '*Doumo arigatou gosaimashita*,' everyone repeats, happy and full of energy.

2 THE LIBYAN SYBIL

If you look closely at some of the large figures on the ceiling of the Sistine Chapel, you may notice something peculiar. A good number of them have books in their hands. It appears they want to read. Mischievous kids are close by. (Figs. 3, 4).

Fig. 3.

Fig. 4.

'Could it be Michelangelo wanted to read but never had the time?' I ask a roomful of modern dancers at Temple University in Philadelphia.

'When I was a modern dancer, I wanted to read too, but I was either in technique class or rehearsing. I remember seeing a bumper sticker that read, *I'd rather be dancing*. I knew, straight away, that person was not a dancer. If they were a dancer their bumper sticker would have read, *I'd rather be reading*.' Lots of knowing smiles appear all around me.

Fig. 5.

'There was one figure on the ceiling of the Sistine Chapel that stood out to me, that mesmerized me, that possessed me, that became my muse, and soon thereafter the logo for the Alexander Alliance. She was the Libyan Sybil (Fig. 5).

'Why do you think I chose her? What might be the connection between the Libyan Sybil and the Alexander Technique?'

She's beautiful.

She's strong.

She's poised.

She's got a great back.

She's spiraling.

Once I feel students have seen what they are going to see, then, if there is more I want to direct their attention toward, I will.

'Notice how Michelangelo figures often appear androgynous. As men undo their culturally acquired masculine holding patterns, often they feel more feminine. And as women undo their culturally acquired feminine holding patterns, they sometimes feel more masculine. I move people away from their acquired gender bodies and into what I call their mammal body, the body that men and woman share, their human body.

'Can you see that the Libyan Sybil has a beautifully synergistic flexion of the hips, knees and ankles? We want that happening in conjunction with an expanding back that emanates power through the arms, into the hands, and through the spine, into the pelvis and the skull. And the Libyan Sybil has got all that going for her.

'I also love her arms. They remind me so much of Marj Barstow's arms, my teacher's arms, when she worked with us. Marj's scapulae were wide. Her shoulders were neither up nor down, more just out and away, one from the other. Her elbows and wrists were articulate. When Marj worked behind a person, with her hands lightly touching the sides of their neck, her elbows were ever so slightly back and out, creating room for her arms and torso, while her wrists were going in slightly toward the mid-line, and forward. It all looked very elegant and effortless. And strong. Even though Marj was in her seventies and eighties when I studied with her, and had her arms out in front of her all day long, her arms never seemed to tire. It was as if her arms rested on the air, suspended, just like the Libyan Sybil's arms.

'Then there's that exquisite spiraling throughout her body that you've noticed. Let's look more closely at what is going on there. There's a descending spiral, and an ascending spiral. The descending spiral begins with the head and eyes. Something's got her attention; something's turning her attention away from her book. The descending spiral is primarily concerned with orientation. You hear something, or you see something, and your orientation shifts.

'Now what about the ascending spiral? From where is that initiating?'

From her hips.

'Lower.'

From her left foot.

'Lower.'

From the ground.

'That's what it looks like to me, from the ground, and then sequentially up through the body. So if the descending spiral is about orientation, what's the ascending spiral about?'

Maybe action. It's helping her to hold up the book.

Power to do what she's doing.

Support.

'That's how I see it too. She's got support from the ground and power from her whole body under that book, and then something gets her attention and Michelangelo catches her just at that moment of transition. Why would he want to do that?'

Because it looks cool.

'The cool factor is very important. The Libyan Sybil is a super cool figure. Just imagine how incredible the Sistine Chapel was when the first people ever to enter that room looked up and saw these huge three-dimensional-looking figures almost falling out of the ceiling. Painting was not Michelangelo's thing. He was a sculptor. He was forced to paint the Sistine Chapel. So he discovered new techniques for making his two-dimensional figures appear three-dimensional.

'Michelangelo likes that transitional moment. We don't really know what the Libyan Sybil is doing or why. Is she opening the book or closing the book? There's mystery. There's action. She's in motion. Michelangelo's not painting form, but motion and emotion. He's a motional and emotional anatomist. He's a storyteller.

'When you really think about it, there aren't two spirals. There's just one. Take your sweater or leg warmer, something that you can use to perform a wringing motion. Now, imagine that what you are holding is a soaked towel. Hold the top of the towel with your left hand, and the bottom with your right hand. The top is the head. Now, slowly turn your bottom hand clockwise and watch the ascending spiral go all the way to the top. That's the power spiral. Then gently counter that action by turning your top hand counter-clockwise. That's the orientating spiral. Imagine turning it so gently that no water is squeezed out of the towel. When we strongly wring out a wet towel, our spirals turn into a twist. An area is created where both movements oppose one another and stop each other, creating torsion. But if the spiral is gentle enough, and if it moves through the whole towel, there will be no conflict, no blockage, just one integrated spiraling motion occurring in two complimentary opposing directions.

'The Libyan Sybil, for me, is the symbol of a person who can gracefully transition, change direction, change opinion, adapt, without losing poise, without disturbing herself. Imagine being a parent who is trying to do something, like read, or cook, or pay the bills, and your two young children have just started physically fighting with one another. How are you inside of that transition? How gracefully can you shift your attention? How do you adapt to changing circumstances?

'I am going to compare our Libyan Sybil to another figure, one of the Ignudo figures (Fig. 6), one of the 20 naked, muscular male figures in the Sistine Chapel. By contrasting these two figures you will end up seeing and understanding both of them better than if you had looked at them separately. Let's look.

'What is he feeling, and what specifically tells you what he is feeling?'

Fig. 6.

He's panicking. His eyes are bulging out. It looks like he's gasping. Even his hair contributes to this sense of panic.

Worried. Something about how his forehead is raised and his eyebrows are dropping down.

Dreading something. I really don't know. I feel it through his whole body. Maybe it's in his back and neck and shoulder. And the way his upper lip is pulled up. Something bad is happening.

Really sad. It could be the angle of his eyes, or the tilt of his head or the sunken feeling in his chest.

Feeling hopeless. The chest and eyes.

Feels threatened. It looks like he wants to get away. He's looking back but his body is trying to go forward. Maybe.

'Images are like Rorschach tests. We project our inner life onto outer images. Why else would we all be interpreting what we see differently? Let's compare the Ignudo to a sketch of the Libyan Sybil (Fig. 7). Tell me what you are seeing and the feeling it creates.'

Fig. 7.

The scapula is moving down and out and around the ribs. It looks strong and graceful.

The spine looks long. The neck is not compressed or shortened. It creates a feeling of balance and elegance.

The eyelids are lowered; forehead and eyebrows relaxed. That makes her look calm and objective and in control.

The mouth is closed. It makes her seem observant, thoughtful, self-possessed.

The head, instead of tilting back, is tilting ever so slightly forward. I don't know, she feels dignified.

Yeah, instead of looking over the shoulder by flipping the head back, the Libyan Sybil is tilting the head forward and rotating her head around her shoulder.

It's amazing. The figures are completely opposite in almost every way.

'That is why I juxtaposed them. You're beginning to see how I see, because you are recognizing the specific physical traits that express the emotion.

'Let's go a step further. Try both ways and see if it changes how you feel emotionally. Do your best to do exactly what they are doing. And once you are being one of them, ever so slowly, ever so gently and softly transform yourself into the other one. And then ever so slowly, go back and forth, being one figure and then being the other figure.'

They get to work. I sit back and watch, one of my favourite ways of getting to know my students.

'So what was that like?'

It's eerie. When I take on the Ignudo, I feel scared. I start to panic. And when I become the Libyan Sybil, I grow calm. Really calm. I feel mature.

Many heads are nodding in agreement.

'Head poise has an organizing, integrative influence, a governing influence throughout the entire "bodyself". And when this head poise is disturbed, disturbance happens throughout the whole "bodyself". That is why a head is called a head. It's in charge. It governs.

'So let's look one more time. What do you see happening to the Ignudo's body?' (Fig. 8.)

Fig. 8.

It looks really uncomfortable. The head is looking back to the right, but the right arm and upper torso is twisting to the left, and the pelvis is falling back and looks weak.

His body looks stuck, disorganized, and confused. Caught in the middle.

His head is in front of his torso, and his right arm too. And maybe that's counterbalancing his torso falling back.

He looks really compressed in his chest and belly, and his mid-back looks like it's pushing back with a lot of force. And his right scapula is rising up toward his ear.

When I look at him, I notice I'm holding my breath.

'That's a good one. That's what I call embodied seeing, or kinaesthetic empathy. Why do you think I sometimes choose to teach people about the body through art instead of through strictly anatomical drawings?'

Because they're beautiful.

Because sometimes people get a little scared around pictures of skeletons?

For some people who are not academically oriented, looking at scientific anatomical drawings might feel like school, like it's going to be difficult, like they are going to have to memorize a lot of names, and then there's going to be a test.

Medical drawings are images of humans that are not alive, not expressive.

'Yes, I want you to begin by seeing, not a body, but a person, how a person is being in their entirety.

'I want you to see a person's beauty, and through that beauty I want you next to see and sense their humanity. I haven't seen a person who wasn't beautiful in 35 years. And often, the more distraught, the more beautiful.'

A felt silence fills the room. I watch the students as they begin looking at one another through Michelangelo's eyes.

I have them seeing how I want them to see. Now we can begin.

3 THE BLUEPRINT

> When an investigation comes to be made, it will be found that
> every single thing we are doing in the work is exactly what is
> being done in nature where the conditions are right, the differ-
> ence being that we are learning to do it consciously.[1]
>
> F. M. Alexander

Where the conditions are right? What does Alexander mean by
'where the conditions are right'?

In *A Sand County Almanac*, Aldo Leopold writes, 'A thing is
right when it tends to preserve the integrity, stability, and beauty
of the biotic community. It is wrong when it tends otherwise.'[2]

Perhaps Leopold is telling us that the way we know we are con-
ducting ourselves in accordance with nature is when we are pre-
serving our integrity, stability, and (inner) beauty, and that we are
out of balance when we are tending otherwise.

Sir Laurens van der Post, another conservationist, ran wilder-
ness expeditions, taking people who had never had contact with
the wild into the deepest parts of Africa. Van der Post writes:

> If you keep the Earth as close to the initial blueprint of creation
> as you can, and you bring a person into contact with it; a per-

son who is not whole, from a lopsided society - poof - that person changes.[3]

Change the word 'earth' to 'body' and you have:

If you keep the body as close to the initial blueprint of creation as you can, and you bring a person into contact with it; a person who is not whole, from a lopsided society – poof – that person changes.

To keep the body close to the initial blueprint of creation we need an understanding of that blueprint, a working knowledge of our inherent design.

Perhaps naturalists, conservationists, and ecologists have something to teach us about our bodies. Some deep ecologists think of the earth as a living body. I think about the body as moving earth, living landscape, as knowing water, fluid fire. Here I explore Alexander's work as the amateur naturalist I am, as someone who loves and honours nature.

OUR ORIGINAL DESIGN

The illustrations I most often use for my workshops come from *Albinus on Anatomy*, containing prints of Albinus and Jan Wandelaar's famous copperplate engravings made over a period of 20 years in the mid–18th century.

Albinus's figures are alive, animated, and expressive. Layer by layer, Albinus reveals us to ourselves. Wandelaar places Albinus's figures within evocative background settings, directing our eyes to what he wants us to see. They take us ever more deeply into nature as it expresses itself through us. He shows us how we are living palimpsests, layers upon layers of meaning woven into our muscles, etched into our bones.

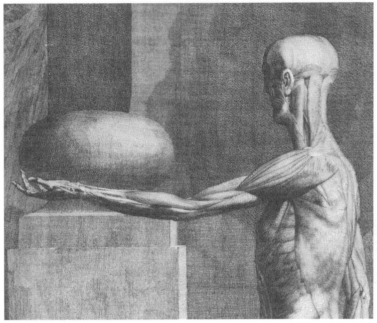

Fig. 9.

THE SKULL

Why is this oblong shape on top of this column not a sphere? (Fig. 9.) This is no accident, not a coincidence. This is a choice. Have you ever seen that shape placed on top of a column? Clearly, Wandelaar wants us to look at it. By the way he has placed the figure's hand under the oblong shape, he is almost serving it to us on a silver platter. What does Wandelaar want to direct our attention toward within the figure? Notice where the light and shadows fall on the oblong shape and then notice where they fall on the figure's skull. There it is, the oblong skull resting atop the column-like neck. As plain as the nose on your face, so to speak.

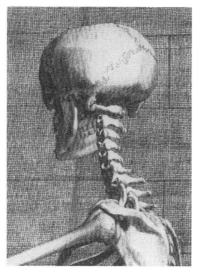

Fig. 10.

Albinus also wants us to take a close look at the skull (Fig. 10). Here Albinus wants us to see that almost half of the skull is behind the weight-bearing part of the spine. Or conversely, that the spine is further in front of the back of the skull than we might suspect. He does this by having us look at the skeleton from a particularly revealing angle. He wants to make it clear to us that the skull, jaw, and spine are three distinct skeletal systems. He wants us to see that half of the cervical spine exists unseen behind the jaw.

Let's go back to 1489, to Albinus's anatomical predecessor, Leonardo da Vinci. In medieval times they were already onto the importance of the brain (Fig. 11). They saw it as having three chambers where our intellectual and imaginative powers as well as our memories are stored. The brain was also thought to be the centre from which human motion and emotion were transmitted. It was the complex within which the entire nervous system both

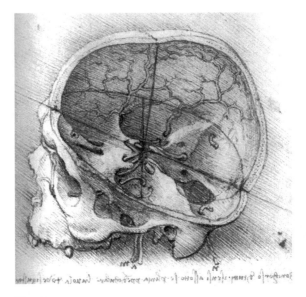

Fig. 11.

emanated and converged. Every voluntary action was controlled from the brain, all gross and fine motor movement. Da Vinci called this centre the *sensus communis*.

But da Vinci went a step further. He writes:

> The soul seems to reside in the judgement, and the judgement would seem to be seated in that part where all the senses meet, called the *sensus communis*, and is not all-pervading throughout the body, as many have thought. Rather it is entirely in one part.

THE SACRUM
Let's return to the eighteenth century and to Albinus and Wandelaar.

When I show this image (Fig. 12) to my students almost no one sees what I see, until I point it out to them. After I do, it seems

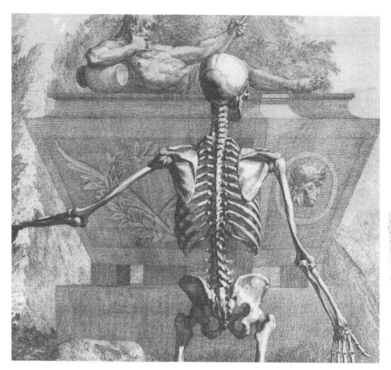

Fig. 12.

obvious to them.

What is it, a tomb? And why the pensive, weighty man resting on top of the tomb? And what of the tomb resting upon bricks, resting upon a huge slab resting upon the ground? And why is the tomb shaped like a keystone? And what is a keystone?

A keystone is a wedge-shaped stone, the final stone that locks all the stones of an arch structure into position, making it able to bear weight – like the sacrum, wedged between the ilia, locking them into place, so the weight of the entire upper body can stably rest and pass through the arch-like structure of the pelvis and legs, into the ground.

Fig. 13.

THE HEELS

The heels, like the back of the skull and the sacrum, also exist in the dorsal plane, the back third of the body, a plane Alexander knew to be a source of great support and power.

Why are those rocks shaped the way they are (Fig. 13)? What does Wandelaar want us to see? (By now my students are getting good at this game.) The heel, of course, the calcaneus, particularly the back of the calcaneus. He wants us to see that the entire heel is below and behind the ankle, or that the ankle is in front of and above the heel.

Perhaps we can say it this way: if you keep a person's understanding of the body as close to the initial blueprint of creation as you can, and you then bring a person into felt contact with the truth of their original design, a person who is not whole, from a lopsided society – poof – that person will change.

Albinus shows us the truth of our design. Alexander's work helps us, via touch, to come into experiential contact with that truth, and it is the truth itself, felt and understood, that frees us, not force, not our will, but simply the truth. Hence Van der Post's word, 'poof' , implying an effortless, sudden, and almost magical personal transformation.

BIOREGIONS

Let's use one more Albinus etching (Fig. 14) as a way of transitioning and returning to our ecological musings on the body.

My guess is that Albinus wants us to associate the body with life, not with death. Here the angel of life unveils to us a work of art. 'Don't be afraid,' I can hear the angel saying. 'Behold the beauty of nature within you.'

Fig. 14.

The cape has uncovered the skull, the jaw, and the spine, precisely down through the sacrum, including the ilia. But the cape has not uncovered the femoral joints or the legs. It has, of course, uncovered the ribs and the arms, but only the upper arms.

For Alexander this region of the body has a profound governing influence over the quality of our entire coordination. The neck, and the dynamic relationship between the neck and the head, and both of them together in dynamic relation to the entire torso, is for Alexander primary, and the limbs secondary.

Ecologically, a bioregion is an area defined by natural criteria, for example, by the fauna, the flora, and watersheds. Regions can be defined by other criteria as well, political criteria, for example. Nations, not nature, decide where Canada ends and the United States begins.

If we are living landscapes, if we have regions, then how do we define them? Where do we place our boundaries, our borders? For example, how do we define our necks? Do we use natural criteria or do we use other criteria?

THE GROUND OF THE NECK

Most people do not understand their necks as defined by natural criteria, as a bioregion. Most people think of their necks in terms of the clothing they wear. We are the only mammals that wear clothing. We are human beings, but we have turtlenecks.

Let's look for a moment at the muscular-skeletal reality of the neck. The neck muscles are multi-layered and attach onto our skull, onto our jaw, onto our spine, onto our upper ribs, and onto our upper arms. That means our neck muscles attach onto five distinct, yet interdependent, bony systems.

When neck muscles become stiff all the bony systems to which our neck muscles attach are immediately affected. And conversely, when neck muscles return to a freer, more fluid condition, all those bony systems release into movement, all at once, altogether.

This is, I suspect, one reason why Alexander's way into freeing ourselves is through the neck. I don't think it's the only way in, but surely it's one of the great openings into our bodies and beings.

When I finally understood my neck as a bioregion, I began making much more progress within myself, and consequently my students did as well. Instead of thinking primarily about the top of my neck and where and how it joined and moved in relation to my skull, I began to include, equally, the ground of my neck, the root system of my neck. I needed to expand my definition of neck to include all the bony systems to which my neck muscles attached: my skull, my jaw, my spine, my upper ribs, and my upper arms. It makes sense. The neck region, in its entirety, is the only hub in our body where five bony systems meet.

We have not even begun to include other organic domains of the neck – for example, nerves, glands, organs, vessels, arteries, etc. They must wait for another time.

INDICATOR SPECIES

An indicator species is a species in a bioregion that indicates to us there's trouble. If the air pollution becomes critical, certain birds or tree frogs, for example, may begin to die. Those little birds and little frogs are telling us, through their fragility, through their sensitivity, that we are heading in an unwholesome direction. If we listen, if we heed their warning, we can change direction. If we don't listen, we, as a whole being, as a whole body, begin to break down.

Our neck functions as an indicator species for our entire body and being. As our neck becomes ever more sensitive through our work, it picks up trouble early on, letting us know when our biotic community is at risk of losing its integrity, its beauty, its stability.

WINGSPANS, WIDENING RIVERS, HOLY PLACES

Da Vinci's Vitruvian Man (Fig. 15), shows a man standing in the centre of a circle and a square. The man, as he relates to the square, has the fingertips of one hand touching one side of the square, while the fingertips of his other hand are touching the other side of the square. The soles of his feet are touching the bottom of the square, while the top of his head is touching the top of the square. What does that imply?

It's a surprise to new students, that their armspan is as wide as they are tall. This truth is hidden to us because most of us use clothing concepts to define our borders, rather than bioregions. Seams and sleeves have come to define where our arms begin and end.

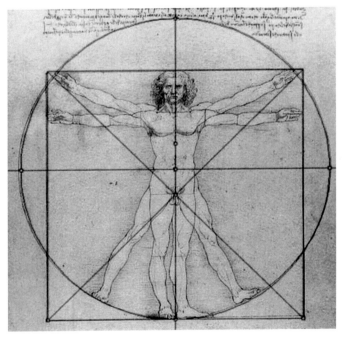

Fig. 15.

Anatomically, bird wings look a lot like arms. A bird wing has a scapula, a shoulder joint, a humerus, an elbow, an ulna, a radius, a wrist, metacarpals, and phalanges.

If we could fly and experience our five- or six-foot wingspan, we'd likely experience the immensity and power of our armspan. But we don't fly. We mostly type or text.

Imagine your arm structure as a widening river. The bones of our arms are not straight, they're spiraled. That's no coincidence. Embryologically, we come out of water. We are sculpted by water.

> Through the limbs whole systems of currents stream, and the muscle more or less follows them. Both muscles and vessels speak of streaming movement in spiraling forms. This movement runs through the sinews into the bones. The bone has raised a monument in 'stone' to the flowing movement from which it originates . . . the liquid has 'expressed itself' in the bone.[4]
>
> *Theodor Schwenk*

Most of us have erected dams, constructed of tension, that interfere with the natural fluid motion of our arms. Often we build large dams in our shoulders and this prevents the river from flowing freely down from its headwaters through the scapulae and clavicles all the way into the elbows, forearms, wrists, hands, into the finger lakes.

My Native American friends tell me that where two rivers meet is a holy place. That's true within us too. Within the ground of our necks, where our widening river meets our lengthening river, is a place of profound confluence and vitality.

There is no doubt that our body is a molded river.[5]

Novalis

Fig. 16.

INCOME INEQUALITY

Each individual body is a microcosm of our collective body. Income inequality translates to tonal inequality. As we become structurally unbalanced, muscle tone becomes unequally distributed. Some muscle groups become hypertonic and others hypotonic. Some areas of the body hoard power while other areas of the body are left lifeless and depleted. Rather than the body governing itself harmoniously, the body descends into chaos. It begins breaking down. It's working against every move it makes. It's at war with itself. Pain and suffering ensue. Injury and illness follow.

Look at healthy six-month old babies and you will see a body where tone is evenly distributed, a homogeneous distribution of tone. They look round, like balls. Everything is filled out.

As we grow up, we more or less lose our even distribution of tone.

THE NORTH-SOUTH DIVIDE

Another way of looking at income inequality and the unequal distribution of attention and tone throughout the global and individual human body is to see it as a division between North and South.

The belt creates an illusory part of the body we have all come to believe exists. It creates a North-South divide. It creates a waist. We have become obsessed with a part of the body that does not exist. We are the only mammals, to my knowledge, that believe we have waists. Look at whales and find the waist. Look at a cat, a dog, a deer, a monkey, or a horse. Look up 'waist' in *Gray's Anatomy* and tell me if you find anything. Our fellow mammals do not have waists because they do not wear clothes. They don't know or care about how they look. Can you imagine? In reality we are indivisible, cannot be divided. We have one whole body. That's it.

Part of my job, as I see it, is to help my students unlearn their culturally acquired physiological divisions so they can once again experience their mammal body, their natural body, their initial blueprint. Perhaps Wandelaar had something like this in mind when he drew the background to Figure 17.

The reality of the psoas replaces the myth of a waist. The psoas, deep and powerful muscles, connect our legs, through our pelvis, to our spines. Instead of an illusionary, superficial, horizontal divide, there is an actual, deeply connecting, vertical bridge. This idea that the North is superior and above, and that the South is inferior and below has got to go. Look at the Earth from the moon. Does a sphere have a North and a South? Does a sphere have an above and a below?

The psoas contributes to our longitudinal support. It facilitates our being vertically locomotive mammals. Maybe this is what Albinus and Wandelaar are telling us, that we are vertical mammals. Here the relationship between human and animal looks tranquil, friendly, peaceful. We live within the animal kingdom and the animal kingdom lives within us.

Rather than thinking about ourselves as created in the image of God, it might serve us better, now, in these times, to think of ourselves as created in the image of Nature.

We've created a disembodied concept of soul, disconnected from the biological world. We've separated matter from spirit. If matter is without soul, unholy, then it can be exploited, abused, and discarded.

What we have done to ourselves we have done to the Earth, and what we are doing to the Earth we are doing to ourselves. How could it be any other way?

How do we bring about right conditions? How do we restore the integrity, stability and beauty of the planet, our larger body? How do we recover our own integrity, stability, and beauty? Can we change direction? Can we restore the soul to its rightful place?

These are not questions to answer. These are problems to solve.

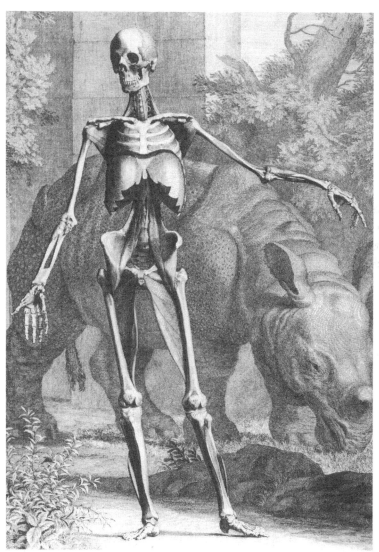

Fig. 17.

When an investigation comes to be made, it will be found that every single thing we are doing in the work is exactly what is being done in nature *where the conditions are right*, the difference being that we are learning to do it consciously.[6] [My italics.]

F. M. Alexander

A thing is right when it tends to preserve the integrity, stability, and beauty of the biotic community. It is wrong when it tends otherwise.[7]

Aldo Leopold

4 OVER TOKYO BAY

It got me fired. A man, a father to one of the young gymnasts at the Mann Recreation Center in Philadelphia where I worked as a gymnastic coach for a girls' gymnastic team, was complaining about how kids in Philadelphia are not as intelligent as they were twenty years ago. At the time, I was 22 years old. 'How do you know that?' I asked.

'Look, I've been teaching for 20 years; high school chemistry. I use the same text book. I cover the same material. My tests are exactly the same as they were 20 years ago,' he says.

'Interesting,' I replied. 'Tell me, have you factored yourself into the equation? I mean, is it possible that after 20 years of changing absolutely nothing, it could mean that you have learned nothing new since then about chemistry, or about teaching? Could it mean you are bored, uninspired, uninspiring, and since you have come to the irrefutable conclusion that kids are not as intelligent as they once were, that you treat them that way, and the kids pick that up and don't listen to you, and don't respect you because you don't respect them?'

'What do you know,' he said in disgust. 'You're just a kid yourself.'

Yes, I was a cocky, arrogant kid with a lot to learn. But I was a good coach. This man was, however, on the board and donated a lot of money to the team. So I was fired. I landed a job a week later teaching for Senior Wheels East Late Start Program, a program that went into the poorest neighborhoods in Philadelphia delivering food to the housebound, providing daily lunches at a number of community centres for the poor and the homeless, as well as offering group activities and classes. My class was a safety in movement class. I'd never taught the elderly but I was a graduate student in the college of HPERD: health, physical education, recreation and dance, at Temple University. I listened to their needs. I experimented. Saw what worked, what didn't. I enjoyed them, learned from them, and figured it out as I went along. But that is a story for another time.

Forty-two years later, still teaching human movement, I walk into my class in Tokyo. I've been developing some new material. I want to try introducing my work centred around a new theme. I'm excited to have the opportunity.

Ohayo gosaimasu, I say bowing to everyone. Everyone, loud and in unison, bows and returns my greeting. There's a lot of energy in the room.

'Why is it so important? I mean, why would His Holiness the Dalai Lama say to us that his religion is kindness? Why, given all the words there are in the world, would he choose the word "kindness"? What does that word mean?'

People are wondering why I am talking about kindness. They are here to be introduced to the Alexander Technique. But I have a way of taking the long way around to get to where I'm going.

'In the English language the word "kind" has two distinct meanings, seemingly unrelated. One meaning is "type". For example, there are two main kinds of screwdrivers we use in America, a slot head and a Phillips. A slot head fits into a screw that has only one straight indentation across the middle of the screw, and a Phillips fits into a screw with two indented crisscrossing lines running through it. Do you have slot head and Phillip screwdrivers in Japan?' They nod yes, wondering why this is important.

I draw the screwdrivers onto my whiteboard. I love scribbling on whiteboards.

'Have you ever needed a little Phillips screwdriver, but all you could find was a big slot head screw driver? But you tried to screw in the screw anyway? You risk three not so great things happening. One, you might damage the screw. Two, you might damage the screwdriver. And three?' Everyone is thinking. I wait. Finally, one person says, 'Maybe you could end up hurting yourself.'

'Right. Okay. Imagine this. You go up to a dog that looks friendly.' Now some of the students may be considering the possibility of my suffering from a mild form of dementia. 'You stand in front of the dog and reach down to pet the top of his head. The dog ducks his head down away from your hand. He doesn't read this gesture as friendly. One, you are much, much higher up, basically towering over the dog. Two, you're standing straight in front of the dog, blocking his means of escape. And three, your big hand, which is not even a paw, is coming down directly over the top of his head.

'Canines are a different kind of mammal from Homo sapiens. They have different ways of greeting one another. If you are a dog the friendly way to approach another dog is not to approach square on but to begin circling around to the side, lowering your head and politely sniffing the other dog's butt, while gladly offering your butt to be sniffed in return. That's friendly and feels safe to a dog.

'Now, if you tried to greet a fellow Homo sapiens that way, with that friendly canine gesture, it most likely would be misinterpreted, perhaps even considered slightly rude.' My first really hearty laughter from the students. That's important.

'Even now, with people I know well here in Japan, if I say hello to them and give them a friendly American hug, they get uncomfortable. They pretend they like it, but I can feel how their bodies get stone rigid. They don't like it. So, almost always, I just bow.

'This brings me to the other meaning for the word "kind". To be kind also means to be considerate and respectful of something or someone.

'So when you understand and take into consideration the kind of thing or creature you are relating to, then you can treat that thing or creature kindly, with respect, the way it wants to be treated.'

'If I want to treat my screw and screwdriver respectfully, I need to understand their design and use them according to their design. That is considerate. That is respectful. That is kind.

'If I want to be considerate and respectful of a dog, I need to know something about dogs. Then I will choose to move slowly, to come down to his eye level, lowering my gaze, positioning myself slightly to the side of the dog. I'll wait for the dog to move slightly toward me, then slowly bring my hand, turned down, making it look more like a paw, up under its chin. That is considerate. That is respectful. That is kind.

'When I am in Japan, a particularly different kind of culture from America, if I want to be considerate, if I want to be respectful, it's best to greet people in a way that makes them comfortable. That's the kind thing to do.

'Now that we know both definitions of the word "kind", and how they are related, the question arises, how do I go about treating myself kindly?

'Alexander's work is founded upon this question; how do I go about treating myself kindly? My mentor, Marjorie Barstow, once said to us, "One day you wake up and say, 'I'm tired of mistreating myself.' That's when you start making some progress." As a young man, and as an actor, Alexander needed to figure out how he was mistreating his voice. He used the word "use" instead of "treat", and "misuse" instead of "mistreat". I like the word "treat" because it has an ethical connotation. It's not purely about function. Later Alexander's inquiry became not only about his voice, but about himself as a person. In other words, his work became about how do humans mistreat themselves. And what do we need to understand and to master to be able to treat ourselves with consideration and with respect?'

After 20 minutes, I have arrived where I want to be. I've explained what Alexander's work is about. I have done it in a way that is simple and easy to understand. I have done it in a way that has made the students think about themselves, not so much about their bodies, just about themselves as people. I can hear them asking themselves, 'Do I mistreat myself? Am I ready to stop mistreating myself?' I have them where I want them.

'For us to learn how to treat ourselves respectfully, there are five facets of life worth considering: time, space, contact, movement, and people.' I seize the opportunity to write them on the whiteboard. 'I choose these because we are always living in relation to them. This is what this workshop will be about.

'We live in *time*. We have to deal with clock time, with being on time, with getting things done on time. And there is psychological time. Do we feel we are running out of time? Do we feel we are wasting our time? Is it the right time for me to tell this person how I feel, or not?

'We are always relating to *space*, the space around us and the space between us and things, like our electronic devices. There is psychological space, space within. Do we feel trapped? Hemmed in? Up against the wall? Do we have room to think, to breathe?

'We are always in *contact*. We sit in a chair at our desk, or in a car, or on the train. We walk down the street, our feet touching the ground with every step. We put food in our mouths. We touch our touchscreens and our keyboards. We handle objects all day long, and lie on our beds or futons every night.

'We *move* continually from the moment we are conceived until the moment we die.'

'And whether we are alone or not, we are never alone. As James Hillman says, we are "our communities internalized". Memories of our parents, critical thoughts about our boss, worries about our children.

'For me as an Alexander teacher, this is the work at hand. If we can learn to create *time* and *space* for ourselves, if we can learn to make respectful *contact* with everything we touch and that touches us, if we can learn to *move* in accordance with our structural design, then perhaps this acquired composure, balance, and sensitivity will carry over into how we relate to *people*, for most of us the biggest challenge of all.

'So when His Holiness the Dalai Lama says, my religion is kindness, I suspect he knows that this is no easy matter. I suspect he knows that to be truly kind requires knowledge, understanding, and devoted practice, and that this practice never ends.'

The silence and the stillness in the room is palpable.

'Okay. Let's have some fun. Actually, let's have a lot of fun this weekend!'

The weekend goes unexpectedly well. Lots of new material emerges. I say things in ways I have never said before. I hear ideas I've never heard before. I use my hands in ways I've never used them before. I teach movements I've never taught before. I've got to know people I never knew before. I've learned a lot this weekend. It seems the students have learned a lot too. There's a lightness in the room. I'm happy.

I pack up my things, looking forward to dinner, to a beer, to being with my friends. It's beautiful outside. The sun is setting over Tokyo Bay. The thought crosses my mind: 'Gee, students seem to be getting smarter with each passing year. They're more open. They learn more quickly. They enjoy themselves more. In fact, they seem friendlier, kinder, and more respectful then ever.'

Kindness is my religion. I'm a devotee for life.

5 MEDITATIONS ON
THE SENSORY WORLD

The spirit is as much at home in the senses as the senses are at home in the spirit; and whatever takes place in the spirit must enkindle a subtle, extraordinary play in the senses. And also the other way around.[8]

Nietzsche

Today I want to do something I don't usually do. I want to give a lecture on what Alexander referred to as sensory appreciation. He wrote about kinaesthesia, about the need for us to re-educate our kinaesthesia, making it more conscious, refined, and accurate. Inaccurate kinaesthesia is like using a uncalibrated compass. If you believe your compass is accurate when it isn't, every directional decision you make will be off. Chances are, before long you will find yourself lost. You won't know where you are.

The first step to getting where you want to go will be to recalibrate your compass. You may have to ask someone to help you do this, or better yet, to teach you how to do this.

John Dewey's term for sensory appreciation was 'sensory consciousness'. We might also call it sensory intelligence.

There are three senses most people know little about. They're rarely acknowledged or consciously cultivated. They're vital to us and we could not live without them. They're senses that tell us more about ourselves than about the world. We hardly learn anything about them in school, not even their names.

Perhaps we don't know much about them because long ago many religions began belittling the body, sometimes to the point of perceiving the body as vile, even demonic. The soul or spirit became an independent entity. The spirit became higher and holy, the body lower and lowly. The spirit was ethereal and eternal, the body material and transitory.

That which was material was of less worth, soulless, and therefore subject to abuse. Those who cared for and nurtured the material world, which included our physical bodies, also became of less worth. Today, people who use their hands to do their work are considered inferior to those who don't. Personally, I'm proud that I use my hands in my work. Ironically, it took an esteemed Professor of Education from Harvard, Howard Gardener, author of *Frames of Mind*, to remind us there were myriad forms of intelligence: musical-rhythmic, visual-spatial, verbal-linguistic, logical-mathematical, bodily-kinaesthetic, interpersonal, intrapersonal, naturalistic, and existential.

Perhaps another reason we don't know much about these senses is due to how much the scientific model influenced the modern world. Science entails the systematic study, through observation and experimentation, of the structure and behaviour of the physical world.

As for arriving at objective knowledge of subjective experience, science finds itself on shakier ground.

Another reason we know little about these three hidden senses is because modern society has virtually deified what I refer to as 'the cosmetic body,' encouraging a preoccupation with how we look. We spend billions upon billions of dollars on jewelry, on clothes, on make-up, on perfumes, on hair products, on skin lotions, on reducing fat, on developing our large muscle groups, our biceps, and pecks, our abs, traps, and quads. This draws attention away from appreciating how our bodies work and how they feel. The cosmetic body distracts us from noticing and feeling what our real bodies do for us, how devoted they are to us, how they continually serve us, how they do everything within their power to keep us alive.

Our institutions of learning lack the knowledge and the sophistication needed to educate our children about how their bodies work, how to take care of them, how to use them, how to respect them, and how to love them. Sports don't fulfill this need. Fortunately, as adults, we can choose to round out our education.

The intrapersonal senses, the senses that inform and track what is happening within us, are the kinaesthetic, proprioceptive, and tactile senses. These senses help us to know where we are (location), how big or small we, or parts of us, are (size), how much tension, pressure, and effort we are exerting (tone), if and how we are moving (kinaetics), how we are feeling (emotion), and even what it feels like to be us, our sense of self (identity).

Though physiologists tend not to distinguish kinaesthesia and proprioception because they are so interrelated, I do. For educational purposes I choose to define them literally. 'Kinaesthetic' means feeling movement or appreciating movement. 'Proprio', as in 'property', means that which belongs to you, so proprioception literally means being able to perceive that which is you and that which is not.

These senses tell us how we feel to be where we are, doing what we are doing, as we are doing it. Neurologists and physical, speech, and occupational therapists know a good bit about these senses, because when these senses are impaired, like when a person suffers a major stroke or a severe spinal injury, everyone knows life is going to get beyond difficult. People get acutely disoriented, often depressed. They can't do a lot of things they took for granted, like knowing where their limbs are, or being able to lift an arm, or hold a fork, or dress themselves, or speak, or balance. Therapists will then work as best they can to restore these senses, an honourable and not always possible task.

Oliver Sacks, in *The Man Who Mistook His Wife for a Hat and Other Clinical Tales*, tells the story of Christina, a woman who, for reasons unknown, suddenly lost her proprioceptive sense. She could not stand up unless she looked down at her feet. Her hands floated around without her knowing where they were unless she was watching them. She dropped things. She had no felt sense of her body. Her breathing had become shallow. In order to sit up she had to hold herself up consciously. The moment she stopped deciding to sit up, she'd collapse like a rag doll.

Proprioception is like the eyes of the body. Christina's body had become blind to itself. But she also lost vocal tone and support as well as facial expression, though she could still feel her full range of emotions.

Christina explained to Oliver Sacks that she felt her core had been scooped out of her. She felt pithed, like a frog. And without this felt sense of her core and of her periphery, she felt she no longer knew who she was, she had lost her sense of self, her identity. Christina had become a disembodied person.

Sir Charles Scott Sherrington, a Nobel laureate, thought of Alexander's work in terms of proprioception. Sherrington discovered proprioception in the 1890s. He referred to it as the secret sense, the hidden sense, or the sixth sense.

We are taught that touch is one of the five senses that tell us about the world. This is true. But touch, like all our senses, is multi-functional. Touch also tells us about ourselves, because all touch is mutual, 100 percent of the time. The fact that we perceive ourselves as touching things in the world, without sensing that whatever we are touching is simultaneously touching us back and giving us information about ourselves, is because of the almost exclusive value we place on the external world to the neglect of intrapersonal life. Touch physically connects us to the world. It's our sense of togetherness, of closeness, of intimacy, of union and communion.

What would happen if we were able to go from having adequate tactile, kinaesthetic, and proprioceptive senses to having extraordinarily tactile, kinaesthetic, and proprioceptive senses? What if these senses became exceptionally accurate, reliable, open, refined, and awakened? What if we became capable of using our intrapersonal senses that tell us about ourselves: kinaesthesia, proprioception, and internal touch, with our interpersonal senses, our senses that tell us about all that is not us: sight, hearing, taste, smell, and external touch? What if we could bring about an integration of all our senses? How would we experience the world? What would it feel like to be alive, to be us?

In 1793, the English poet William Blake wrote in *The Marriage of Heaven and Hell*:

Man has two real existing principles Viz.: a Body & a Soul. *False.* *True*: Man has no Body distinct from his Soul for that call'd Body is a portion of Soul discern'd by the five Senses, the chief inlets of Soul in this Age.

And also:

If the doors of perception were cleansed every thing would appear to man as it is, Infinite. For man has closed himself up, till he sees all things thro' narrow chinks of his cavern.[9]

William Blake

Okay. That's a lot of talking. But there is more. Let's take a 20 minute intermission. If you are interested in what some other great mystics thought about sensory life, come back.

'Okay. What's a Movement Meditation? What do you think?' I ask my class.

It's when you're doing some kind of movement and you drop into the zone, like when shooting hoops, or doing aikido, or running, or rock climbing.

I don't think it has to be anything really fancy. Maybe I could be immersed in what I'm doing when I'm folding my laundry, or raking the leaves in my back yard.

'Good examples. How about Kinaesthetic Contemplation? What's that?'

It could be when we are having a new sensation within us, a moving sensation, and we want to understand it, we want to know where it's coming from, how it's changing us, and what it means. So that makes it a form of contemplation.

'Sounds good to me. How about a Senso-Spiritual Practice? We're getting weirder and weirder.'

I think this one is simple. It's like you're taking a walk and you see a black-eyed Susan and you stop and look at it for a while. You see this incredible geometric pattern and you smell its perfume and feel how powdery soft it is and you get this feeling of it being totally miraculous, this simple flower. It almost makes me cry just thinking about it.

'I love that example. Can someone give me another example?'

When I play Bach sonatas, which I do almost every morning. Even though Bach wasn't very religious, I hear something that feels sacred to me, like a river running into the sea. It's hard to explain, but as the years go by, and the more I practise, the stronger this feeling gets. And this feeling opens me up. I think it actually makes me more loving.

'Wow. That almost makes me cry just thinking about it. Anything else?'

Something happens to me when I get up early and go birdwatching with my birder friends. The air is cool and fresh, and here we are looking for these little birds, and some of them are so beautiful, like an indigo bunting, or a western tanager. And most of the time I'm so busy I just pass this beautiful world by. But when I'm birdwatching my senses get finely tuned, my hearing, my seeing. Even my movements change. I can be still and silent for a very long time. And for some reason, at a certain moment, something comes over me and I feel grateful to be alive on the earth. I go home, and my wife and kids are just getting up, and I feel great. I'm in a great mood.

'You see, maybe this one is not weird at all. Maybe the sensory world and the spiritual world go hand in hand, and maybe it's so obvious we just miss it. Maybe this notion that the senses are physical and the spiritual is mental isn't quite right. We go looking for our spirituality, God knows where, and there it is surrounding us all the time. Maybe by better attending to our senses we can more easily find entrance into the spiritual world. Sometimes I get sad thinking how little most cultures spend on the arts because art is a great way into senso-spiritual life, and nature is too.

'Once, many years ago now, I was invited to Omega Institute in Upstate New York to teach a five-day workshop. All the teachers who were giving workshops met the day before to get to know one another a little. A woman with the bluest, wisest eyes, a deep ecologist by the name of Joanna Macy, was there. And a man, a tracker by the name John Stokes was there with a few of his apprentices.

'There was this burly guy with a thick beard, large forearms, and calloused palms who was as soft as a big teddy bear. He came up to me and asked me what I was teaching, and I said something about sensory awareness. He said, "That's very much what I teach too, except I'm not the one who's really teaching my students about

their senses. The woods do that for me. How do you teach your
students about their senses without the woods?"

'Okay. Here's the one no one can answer. What's a Post-Proprioceptive Prayer?'

Silence descends upon the room.

'You're close. Can you say a little more?'

Well, proprioception has something to do with the position we are
in, with knowing exactly where we are. So post-proprioceptive prayer . . .
hmm . . . I don't know.

'Let's begin at the beginning. This may take a while. I've got to
go step by step. But it will be worth it, so hang in there with me.'

PRE-PROPRIOCEPTION AND PROPRIOCEPTION

'When we are born, so I am told, as I have no conscious memory
of this, we cannot identify what is our body and what is not. We
don't have an identity. We are not an "I". We are a little bundle of
sensation with no awareness that we are a bundle. Maybe Descartes
was right when he said, "I think therefore I am." Maybe there is no
"I am" before we begin thinking. As a newborn we are alive but
we don't know we are alive. It's a mystery to me how we transition from pre-proprioception to proprioception. Here are my musings on the subject.

'Proprioception tells us our *position or shape*, for example it tells
us if our elbow is flexed or straight. Proprioception tells us about
location, where one part of our body is in relation to another part,
and in relation to the body as a whole. Your right arm may be
flexed and you sense its shape, but is it over your head or by your
side? Proprioception tells us about *orientation*. Where is our body in
space? Are we lying down or are we standing up? And some might
say that proprioception tells us if we are moving or not. I tend to
associate movement with the kinaesthetic sense. But in living it is

almost impossible to separate touch, proprioception, and kinaesthesia.

'Close your eyes and slowly touch your nose with your index finger. Sense how you can kinaesthetically feel that your finger is moving but that your nose is not. The only way you are going to have any idea where your nose is, is through your proprioceptive sense.

'So we enter this world and we have no clue about the shape of our body, or of any part of our body. And we've no clue where one part of our body is in relation to another part. And we have not the faintest idea where we are in relation to the environment because we can't tell the difference, we can't differentiate. And as far as whether we are moving or still, well how could we possibly know what is moving, our mother or us, the bed or us? We are pre-proprioceptive.

'But we come out into the world with a great sense of touch. We're transitioning from relating to a fluid environment to a solid environment. We feel this. We start rolling against a hard surface. We're experiencing gravity when we try to lift our formidably large heads. But we're strangers in a strange land. If we're lucky, we have people around who love us and love touching us a lot. We're feeling a little squeeze on our calf, or a kiss on the cheek. Suddenly we are being squeezed around the ribs and lifted high above someone's smiling face. People are putting us in silly looking clothes and increasingly, through almost constant sensorial research, we are, literally, figuring out where we are.'

EXTENDED PROPRIOCEPTION

'Extended proprioception grows out of proprioception. The potential for extending proprioception is built into us, but we also have to work at it. Babies work at it. Children work at it. And adults work at it.

'We extend proprioception when we can get an object to do what we want. It's as if we extend our nervous system into the object, much as amputees with sensorialized prostheses are now able to do. You can watch a baby learn to manipulate a baby bottle, pick up a pea, eventually write with a pencil, button a shirt, tie a shoe, ride a bike, fly a kite, and eventually drive a car. Oh no! You can see how persistently babies and kids work on extending proprioception.

'Extending proprioception can get pretty sophisticated: playing a musical instrument, fencing, fly fishing, kayaking, knitting.

'Not only can we extend our proprioception into objects, which is exciting enough, we can extend our proprioception into creatures as well. When my daughter was hardly a year old I'd take her to see horses at a nearby stable and she'd go wild. In the worst way she wanted to touch those horses and sit on those horses. I'm convinced there's a horsemanship gene. Watch a great equestrian and you will see extended proprioception, two creatures moving as one. Or watch great aikidoists, or great tango dancers.

'This brings us to the relationship between extending proprioception and intimacy. It's no mistake that dancing and courtship go hand in hand. Whether it is swing, or tango, or contact improvisation, most humans love physical intimacy. It doesn't matter whether this physical intimacy is sexual or nonsexual. Physical intimacy brings people literally and figuratively in touch with one another.

'Paradoxically, proprioception helps us to differentiate ourselves from what is not us and, at the same time, it has the potential, when extended, to unite us with others and with the things of this world. It has the capacity, simultaneously, to distinguish and to unify.

'Marjorie Barstow, my mentor, once told me to watch my hands all through the day and see if I ever distorted them. "Bruce, if you catch your hands looking ugly or distorted, if they wouldn't look beautiful in a photograph, then stop right away and you will see that you are distorting your whole body. Wait until you know exactly where you are, the relationship of the parts of your body, one to the other, as well as the shape of your body as a whole, and then release the distortion throughout your entire body and work out a way of using your whole body and your hands without distortion. Because when we are distorted we cannot relate well to anything."

'Marj was talking about proprioception and extending proprioception. Marj's ability to extend proprioception was extraordinarily refined. She knew precisely where she was, so when, as an Alexander teacher, she touched me it was as if I became part of her exquisite nervous system and without any effort I became, like her, beautifully integrated. Her touch was intimate in that her hands did not feel separate from my body. They felt like they were under my skin, not on my skin. Her hands were a part of me. Yet her touch was non-sexual in nature. It was as if Marj was overlapping into me, like one circle intersecting another. We were two people with one nervous system.

'Here is another example, perhaps my favourite, describing communion through touch and extended proprioception. It was written by Jacques Lusseyran, French author and French Resistance leader during World War II:

> Being blind I thought I should have to go out to meet things, but I found that they came to meet me instead. I have never had to go more than halfway, and the universe became the accomplice of all my wishes . . .
>
> If my fingers pressed the roundness of an apple, I didn't know whether I was touching the apple or the apple was touching me . . . As I became part of the apple, the apple became part of me. And that is how I came to understand the existence of things.

As a child I spent hours leaning against objects and letting them lean against me. Any blind person can tell you that this exchange gives a satisfaction too deep for words . . .

. . . Touching the tomatoes in the garden is surely seeing them as fully as the eye can see. But it is more than seeing them. It is the end of living in front of things, and the beginning of living with them.[10]

Jacques Lusseyran

'How are you doing? Are you following me? I don't usually talk this much, but this is a bit complex. Shall I go on?'

I get nods of approval, so I continue.

PRAYER

'Now we have some understanding of pre-proprioception, proprioception, and extended proprioception. Before we can understand post-proprioception, and what a post-proprioceptive prayer is, let's think about what it means to pray, and what is a prayer. Again, these are just my musings on the subject.

'When I was four years old I slept in a little room with a little window near the foot of my bed. My mom would come into my room and we'd pray. Quietly she'd say, and I would say with her, "Now I lay me down to sleep I pray to God my soul to keep, and if I should die before I wake . . ." *If I should die! What is she talking about?* ". . . I pray to God my soul to take." And then finally, "Sleep tight, don't let the bedbugs bite." *Bedbugs! What bedbugs!* After she would leave I was wide awake. To calm down I would do my own praying. I would sit at the foot of my bed, on my knees in seiza, and look up out my window at the few stars I could see. Only one star was red so I decided to pray to that star. A couple of years later, I found out that my red star was a red light sitting on top of a radio tower. That was disappointing.

'I would pray for things I wanted. I remember praying for a puppy dog, and when I finally got my soft, playful puppy, which I adored, I was soon infested with worms, and before I knew it my puppy was gone. After that praying lost some of its appeal.

'It wasn't until I was considerably older, around 30, that I actually began to pray for other people. I no longer believed in a God who could grant wishes, but I found myself wanting to be with people, in my heart and mind, that I cared about, who were in need, as if I were keeping them company.

'Many years later, after a particularly long, dark period in my life, I shifted into a different kind of praying. I completely stopped wishing or hoping for anything, for me or for anyone else. I was beginning to accept and appreciate exactly how things were.

'If I was suffering, or someone else was suffering, rather than making a request I would ask a question. "If God is good, then what is good about what is happening now?" And then I'd become deeply quiet, do nothing, and wait without waiting for any answer. Sometimes the answer would arise almost immediately and at other times not for weeks.

'The more I began to experience everything as good, the more I found myself feeling grateful, often for little things I had up to now taken for granted, like being able to walk, or see, or having work that mattered to me, or that my kids were healthy. Just being alive rather than not, statistically speaking, seemed totally miraculous, and I found myself silently saying thank you almost all day long. And this thankfulness became a new, more mature form of prayer for me. It seemed I was almost in a perpetual state of prayer.

'But there was one more shift yet to happen.

'It's a lot like when you first fall crazy in love with someone. You find yourself intoxicated, under a spell. Everything seems perfect because you are filled with this feeling of being in love with

someone. Instead of writing thank-you letters all day long, I began
writing love letters all day long!'

POST-PROPRIOCEPTION

'Step by step. We are almost there. Now we know what is pre-
proprioception, proprioception, and extended proprioception. We
know what mature prayer is, gratitude and love. Once we know
what post-proprioception is, we can put it all together and you'll
know what I mean by a post-proprioceptive prayer.

'When we extend our proprioception exceptionally well we
find ourselves in a harmonious relationship with an object, tool,
instrument, device, or with nature, an animal or a person. There
are, however, brief moments, when a merging happens, when we
no longer feel as if we are in a relationship. We, as a separate I, are
no longer there. It's a post-proprioceptive moment. It's as if we
have reverted to a pre-proprioceptive condition, *but it's not pre-proprioceptive because we're conscious of it*. Often these moments verge
on the ecstatic.

'Ecstatic, in Greek *ekstasis*, means a dis-placement, a removal
from a proper place. Proper, as in *proprio*, as in property, means *that
which is you*. So a post-proprioceptive moment is a *felt dis-placement
or absence of that which is you*. In colloquial terms, it's a moment
when we are "blown away".

'In Judaism we have a prayer you are supposed to say every
night before going to sleep and, if you are lucky enough, at the
moment you are leaving this world. It's called the Shema. The
Shema means, as a Rabbi once told me, "Listen, you person who
wrestles with God, I will give you a hint. God is one, not two."

'There was a woman with whom I was deeply in love. Sometimes I'd see her and spontaneously a poem would arise in me, fully
formed. All that was left was to quickly write it down and give it
to her. Here's an example of a post-proprioceptive poem or prayer,

written now long ago. Note the element of mergence, a felt displacement, of an absence self, and of gratitude:

> Have you ever been walking in the woods
> Hearing no sound of a stream, and then suddenly you hear it?
> Have you ever been walking for so long in the sound of the
>   stream
> That you cannot imagine how a sound could enter and fill
>   you so completely,
> Leaving no space for words
> Or even for the thought of a stream sounding
> Until the sound, streaming in your veins
> Sends the trees and rocks rolling into white clouds upon a hill
> That meets your back in soft green grass where you land,
> Safely, staring up at the sky, so blue, wondering,
> Not who you are, but that you are?

POST-PROPRIOCEPTIVE PRAYER

'Some people believe that this ability to enter into a post-proprioceptive condition is the basis for all religious sentiment.

'Roman Rolland, a French dramatist, novelist, art historian, and mystic, was awarded the Nobel Prize for Literature in 1915. He coined the term "oceanic feeling". It meant this felt experience of oneness or limitlessness. Freud's opinion was that this oceanic feeling, felt by some people and not by others, was "merely" a carry over of a primitive pre-egocentric feeling, what I would call a pre-proprioceptive condition. Rolland and other mystics would beg to differ. For the mystics this experience of oneness and limitlessness was not "merely" primitive, not only primal but sacred.

'Perhaps there is some connection between the unity a fetus experiences within its mother, the oneness experienced through sexual unity, and the oneness experienced through spiritual unity. God is one, not two.

'Here's a Rumi poem that captures all three experiences of post-proprioception:

> *The Freshness*
> When it's cold and raining,
> you are more beautiful.
> And the snow brings me
> even closer to your lips.
> The inner secret, that which was never born,
> you are that freshness, and I am with you now.
> I can't explain the goings,
> or the comings. You enter suddenly,
> and I am nowhere again.
> Inside the majesty.[11]
>
> *Rumi*

'There you go, a post-proprioceptive prayer of the highest order.

'Another one of my favourite mystics, Meister Eckhart, encourages us to practise shifting out of a proprioceptive condition into a post-proprioceptive condition. For him this is a spiritual practice. Meister Eckhart writes:

> Start with yourself therefore, and take leave of yourself . . . Examine yourself, and wherever you find yourself, take leave of yourself. This is the best way of all.[12]

'Start with yourself. First we have to know where we are. First our proprioception must awaken and become accurate. That doesn't happen all by itself. It takes study and practice.

'And take leave of yourself. What does this mean? What happens to us along the way is that we become "proprioceptively established". We have drawn an outline around where we are, and that outline becomes thicker and thicker and darker and darker, until it becomes like an exoskeleton separating ourselves from all that surrounds us. When this happens we can never change "where we are". We've locked ourselves in and lost the key. We can't get out and nothing can get in. We are in a proprioceptive prison of the self.

'Can we learn, gradually, to make our outline less thick, less dark? Can we learn to erase it? I think we can. You see, it's as if we are living our lives constantly inside of parentheses. What would happen if we could delete our parentheses? Let's look.'

I go up to the whiteboard, pull the top off of a blue magic marker, and begin writing:

This is me.
(bruce fertman)

Without the parentheses, this is me:
bruce fertman

'"Examine yourself, and wherever you find yourself, take leave of yourself."

'We have mistakenly come to identify ourselves with the parentheses that contain us. Take note. Meister Eckhart does not tell us where to go. He simply says, *Examine yourself, and wherever you find yourself, take leave of yourself.* He doesn't say, take leave of yourself and then go here. He doesn't say, take leave of yourself and then do this or don't do that. Our only job is to: one, examine ourselves, know where we are; and two: take leave of where we are. He's having us practice a shifting from a proprioceptive sense of self to a post-proprioceptive way of being with the world.

'"This is the best way of all," he says. Meister Eckhart is saying there is nothing better. This is as good as it gets. That has been my experience too.

'Transitioning from proprioceptive life to post-proprioceptive life is like a cicada metamorphosing out of its shell. One gets the feel of a creature leaving a body grown too small and rigid for who it has become; a creature taking leave of itself.

'Now we can't always experience so dramatic a metamorphosis. Some of us may never experience such a dramatic transformation. To do so usually requires hitting bottom, surviving a dark night, enduring a long Bardo, traversing the seven terraces of purgatory.

'But transformation can be gradual as well. We can, little by little, emerge from ourselves. As Walt Whitman writes in *Song Of The Open Road*, "Gently, but with undeniable will, divesting myself of the holds that would hold me."

'When I work with you that's what I am doing. I'm gently using my hands to help you divest yourself of the holds that hold you. I'm helping you to erase your outline, delete your parentheses, and when this happens I hear some of you sometimes say, "I don't feel like myself. This is not me."

'That's why when I work with you I will sometimes change one side of you and not the other. In other words, I'll help you remove one parenthesis and not the other. I'll ask you to draw an imaginary line down through your centre, dividing right and left, and I'll ask you, "Who are you on this side, and who are you on that side?"'

I write on the board:

(Who are you on this side? And who are you on that side?

'Let me work with some of you now, just on one side, and let's see what happens.' Everyone stands up, and I get to work.

I feel older on this side and younger on the other side.

This person on the left feels scared and that person on the right feels confident.

This person is a fighter, and this person is a listener.

I feel like I'm trying to be invisible on this side, and on this side I want people to see me.

'This is what I mean when I speak of becoming less proprioceptively established. You are beginning to question the establishment, the "static quo". You are unfixed, in motion now, spreading into a free and unknown future, a future not wholly determined by the past.

'Would you like me to give you some post-proprioceptive prayers to take home with you?' 'Yes,' they say. I hand each of them a sheet of paper with seven post-proprioceptive prayers. 'Some of these may be accessible to you and some may not. Play with them for a few weeks and see what happens.'

They begin reading.

One.

Take a walk every day and delete your parentheses as you take in what is all around you. That's simple.

Two

Lie down on the floor, splayed out. Imagine that a friend of yours has a piece of black charcoal. Beginning at the top of your head they start to draw a black outline on the floor, working down one side, tracing around your head, down your neck, along the outside of your arm all the way down to your hand, in and out of each finger, up the inside of the arm, way up into the armpit, down the torso, down the leg, around the heel, up the outside of foot, over the toes, down the inside of the foot, up the inside of the leg, across the pelvic floor, and just keep going until you make your way back to where you began. Sense how that feels, then repeat it two or three times, each time making a thicker and darker outline. Sense how that feels.

Then imagine you are very large, like a large land mass, and all around you in every direction is land that just goes on forever. Hundreds of years go by and gradually the sun bleaches away the dark outline, the winds blow away the outline, the rains wash away the outline until it's completely gone and there's nothing separating you from all that is around you in every direction.

Three

When you are in a train, or a car, or a plane, whenever you happen to find yourself sitting next to a stranger, delete your parentheses. Sense how that feels. Then imagine a large hula hoop and place both yourself and the person next to you inside of the hula hoop and just rest inside the hoop together.

If you are brave enough, sit down next to a person who you feel some aversion toward, a seriously obese person, a mentally or physically challenged person (that's all of us), someone who looks homeless and unkempt, and sit next to them. Delete your parentheses. Sit inside your imaginary hula hoop with them.

Four

You can do the following lying down, or sitting, or standing, or walking, which basically is all humans do. Imagine, and when I say imagine I don't mean seeing a picture on the movie screen inside your head, I mean kinaesthetically imagine the movement within your body, and proprioceptively imagine your shape changing. Imagine your whole body is bread dough rising, rising omnidirectionally, getting lighter and more spacious within itself.

Five

This one is good when sitting, but feel free to experiment. Imagine your whole body is a sponge. Imagine it's soaking up warm water from a deep puddle below and the more it soaks up, the softer and wider and deeper it becomes. There is so much water to soak up, so the water seeps and soaks its way higher and higher as the sponge swells, getting wider and wider, fatter and fatter, fuller and fuller, until the entire sponge can accept no more water. It's important to take this image right up to the very top of your head and beyond.

Six

Imagine, from high above you, sand pouring finely down through a kind of funnel, pouring finely down through your 'whale's spout,' where the soft spot, the posterior fontanelle, is on an infant. Gradually the sand begins to make a little pile on the ground. As the sand continues, which it does for a long time, the little pile gets bigger and bigger. The sides of the pile make a perfect angle of repose. The sand continues to pour down until the point of the pile is about a foot above your head.

Seven

Go for a walk. First sense that the environment is all around you and that you are inside the environment. Walk that way for a while. At a certain moment play with reversing it. Imagine that the entire environment, all you can see and hear and smell, is within you and you are all around it. Everything is in you. See what happens.

'Okay. We are finished for the day. Let me leave you with one last image.'

I get my laptop and bring up a photo (Fig. 18).

'Who would you be without your frame?'

Fig. 18.

I took this photo 20 years ago. It is a remaining wall of a church built around 1744, the Santa Rosa de Lima, a mile south of Abiquiu, New Mexico. I pass it every week on my way down to Santa Fe. One day, as usual, I drive by and the frame is gone. Just gone. I pull over, get out of my old red Jeep and look at what is there without the frame.

'Imagine you are the window frame . . . and who would you be without it?,' I say to my students, who all look decidedly softer and more open than they did when they entered the room this morning.

6 ONE WORD

'What is it about, for you, now? Tell me in one word,' I ask a group
of Alexander trainees and teachers.

Poise.
Stopping.
Vitality.
Support.
Freedom.
Choice.
Awareness.

'Anything else?'

Time.
Grace.
Space.
Living.
Movement.
Ease.
Peace.

'Legend has it a man once asked Alexander if he could tell him,
in one word, what his work was about. What do you think he said?'
No one answers.

'I'll give you a hint. Hamlet.'

No one answers.

'Here's what he said. He said, readiness: "The readiness is all." Hamlet.'

Some trainees and teachers nod their heads. Others look perplexed.

'Marie-Françoise Le Foll, a wise, talented Alexander teacher once told us at the Alexander Alliance that Alexander's work was about being prepared for nothing and ready for anything.

'What does it mean to be prepared and what does it mean to be ready? Are they different? I can see everyone thinking, but no one answers. Perhaps I can help you by way of a story.

'If one lives in New Mexico as I do, reading Tony Hillerman detective novels is a requirement. *The Blessing Way, Dance Hall Of The Dead, Coyote Waits, The Dark Wind . . .*

'Two Navajo Tribal Police, Jim Chee and Joe Leaphorn, are walking around an old trailer where a murder has just taken place. "What are you looking for," Jim Chee asks? "Nothing," Leaphorn answers. "If I'm looking for what I'm looking for, I might miss what I'm not looking for."

'Looking for nothing in particular. Looking for anything that might present itself. Prepared for nothing in particular, ready for anything that may happen. Perhaps that was what Marie-Françoise meant.

'Perhaps it's like the zone a martial artist has to be in when they don't know which way a person or persons will attack, or maybe it's like a woman tango dancer waiting with alert openness, not knowing what her partner will ask of her. Or like an equestrian gathering his horse, bringing his horse into balance under him, collecting the needed alert energy of his horse so that his horse will immediately respond to his slightest direction, though the horse does not know what that direction will be.

'Prepared for nothing in particular. Ready for anything that may happen.

'Thirty years ago, one of my mentors, Buzz Gummere, said to me, "Bruce, I was just taking another look at one of Alexander's books, *Man's Supreme Inheritance*, and in it he states what he is after through his work. Three abilities. One, the ability to adapt rapidly; two, the ability to assimilate new ideas; and three, originality. What do you think about that?"'

I can see my students beginning to put the pieces together.

'My equestrian students have told me a bit about Linda Tellington-Jones and her work with horses. Tellington-Jones observes how horses, when they feel unsafe, either fight, flee, freeze, fidget or faint. We humans do all of these too. I would add one more f-word. We feign, that is, we fake, we fib, we erect façades. We each get especially good at a couple of these survival modes and use them when we feel we need them. When in a threatening situation some of us become aggressive. We survive through some form of fighting. We might be overtly aggressive or passively aggressive, physically aggressive or verbally aggressive. We are crafty animals. We flee, we run away, we withdraw from situations. We find ways of not showing up, not participating, procrastinating, hiding. We freeze, we panic, we become paralyzed with fear, paralyzed by uncertainty, unable to decide, unable to act, like Hamlet. We feign, we fake, we pretend, we deceive. We fidget, that is, we get nervous, we crack our knuckles, bite our nails, tap our feet, touch our faces, twirl our hair. And sometimes we faint. We collapse. We quit, give up, lie down and die. We do our best to survive and, when under duress, our instincts click in and we behave just like other animals.

'That's natural. But for humans something else is also natural. We have an alternative when under duress that other animals don't have. We can respond in another way when we, or those we love, feel unsafe, threatened, constrained, or attacked.

'Imagine you are in a situation where you feel unsafe, threatened, constrained, or attacked. Maybe your boss is placing overwhelming demands upon you, or your partner is criticizing you in a way that feels abusive. Maybe you are lost, walking down a dark, unknown street in a strange city. Maybe your kids are hanging out with kids you don't like, and you're afraid they are binge drinking and getting into unsafe sex. Or you have a job interview tomorrow and you desperately need the job because your savings are depleted and you have fallen into debt.

'Find your situation. Now sit back in your chair. Accept the support your chair is offering you. Give yourself space, lower your eyelids and place yourself in that situation.

'I am now going to ask you a question, and I invite you to sense what happens as you answer it for yourself.'

I wait until I see everyone sitting, supported, and living inside of their difficult situation.

'What would happen if inside of the situation you are in right now, you decided that, no matter what happened, you are not going to fight.' I wait about ten seconds.

That you are not going to run away . . .

That you are not going to panic . . .

That you are not going to be who you are not . . .

That you are not going to fidget . . .

That you are going to remain awake and fully conscious . . .

I wait for about a minute and then I ask, 'What happened?'

My wife was expressing her disappointment in me, and I was able not to defend myself. I just listened.

I do have an interview coming up next week. Just imagining it I got myself so scared. But as I asked each question, especially when I decided not to freeze, I felt myself begin to breathe. I became very calm, and it was just as you said, I felt like I could just be myself and that that would be the best thing I could do.

For me the whole situation I was in disappeared completely and I fell into a deep place where I felt completely peaceful. Oddly my body filled with a kind of power, and when I opened my eyes I felt wide awake, in a way I have not felt before.

'Perhaps these are examples of what readiness sometimes feels like for humans. Being ready doesn't mean we have to possess the physical prowess of a martial artist or athlete. This deep deciding inside of a stressful situation not to engage our more instinctual reactions brings about a stopping, utter and complete, allowing for an intelligent readiness, for a mobility of mind and for physical regeneration, as Alexander describes it.

'Alexander realized that this deep deciding, this utter and complete internal stopping was a requisite for this uniquely human response.

'This is why properly trained and humane law enforcement officers can decide, when attacked, to protect both themselves and their attacker, making sure harm comes to no one. With composed alertness, at once mental, emotional, physical, and spiritual, they can make a decision about how they wish to proceed, even when under a life and death situation.

'Buzz Gummere relayed a story to me about a conversation between John Dewey and Alexander. It was in New York City, during World War I. Alexander told Dewey that the ultimate problem we were facing was within us and not around us. He said that the real war was going on inside of man, between his inhibitors and his exciters, and unfortunately, the exciters were winning.

'Perhaps this is why so many of us feel inspired and in awe of people like Mahatma Gandhi, Martin Luther King, Jr., and Nelson Mandela. And Jesus too. We are moved by people with the self-possession to respond consciously, freely, in touch with their humanity, with their dignity and with the dignity of others inside of life-threatening situations. We want to be like them.'

I ask the trainees and teachers if they now understand why Alexander's one word was 'readiness'.

Every head nods a definitive yes. Their bodies look surprisingly open and strong, dignified and capable, ready for anything that may come their way.

7 WITHOUT OUR HAVING TO ASK

———◆◆◆———

I see at last that if I don't breathe, I breathe.[13]

F. M. Alexander

A student wants to know the right way to breath. I praise him for asking such an important question. Here was my answer.

That's a good question. Once Erika Whittaker* was working with me and I let go of a deep holding pattern. I gave a sigh of relief and she said, 'Bruce, I enjoy listening to your voice, but I don't want to hear your breathing. Breathing is a shared silence, between you and God.'

I'm no expert on breathing, but I will tell you everything I know about it. How's that?

When we enter this world, we do not take our first breath. The air of the world rushes into our lungs. We are breathed.

---

* Erika Whittaker (1911-2004) began receiving lessons when she was eight years old from her aunt, Ethel Webb, one of Alexander's assistants. She joined Alexander's first teacher training program in 1931. I met her in 1986 at the first International Congress of the Alexander Technique, and again at the 4th International Congress of the Alexander Technique in 1994. When teaching in Sydney I invited her to my workshops. My students and I then began a monthly correspondence with Erika, sending her an audio tape filled with questions about Alexander and his work, and about her training. She sent tapes back with her answers which we listened to with rapt attention. I then invited Erika to my training program in Philadelphia where she taught for us for two weeks.

As a child, I remember sitting next to my mom in her red 1952 Chrysler on the way to my grandparents' house thinking, 'I wonder how long I can hold my breath?' I found out, to my dismay, that I didn't have as much control over it as I had hoped.

Breathing is mysterious and elusive. It can be slightly modified by our will, but remains largely an act of grace. Given. We are breathed by forces deep within us and all around us. And just exactly when these forces cease breathing us is, to a profound degree, not within our control. We are not the musician playing an accordion; we are an accordion being played by an unknown musician.

In order to let someone, or some force help us, we must first be able to stop insisting on doing everything ourselves. Unknowingly, we often interfere with breathing without understanding how or why, or even when we do it. So first, it helps to become aware of the particular ways in which we interfere with breathing. This, it turns out, is not so easy. As soon as we begin to set about studying our breath, this very act of studying it begins to change it. Immediately we want to breathe right, or well, or fully. Instantly we superimpose our attempt to breathe better, whatever our idea of that is, on top of our habitual way of breathing. We don't want to catch ourselves doing something wrong. No one does.

Breathing is not about doing something right or wrong; it's about doing and non-doing. See what happens if you quietly decide neither to hold your breath, nor to take a breath. There's no need to decide how much air you need, how big or small a breath should be, how deep an inhale should be, or how long an exhale should last. No one knows these things.

Here's something you can play with. Let's play with it now. Pretend you are falling asleep. Whenever breath wants to leave, just let it leave. Pretend you are falling asleep. There's nothing for you to do, there is nothing you can do that will help. Pretend you are almost asleep. Let the air come in and go out, not at your will, but as it wills.

What would happen if you trusted the world and your body to breathe you and if you just quit breathing for yourself? Breathing is not your responsibility, not your job. Breathing is not yours for the taking. It's not yours at all, nor mine.

Breath is given. If breathing defies being studied directly our only recourse, if we want a way into the mystery of breath, is to study it indirectly. This means looking at the conditions that surround breathing. Breathing responds to pressure of any and all kinds, for example: altitude, pollution, over-stimulation, under-stimulation, danger, as well as safety, comfort, love, a cat resting in your lap.

Breathing responds to internal pressures as well, like exertion, hunger, fatigue, strain, disease, time restraints. Breathing responds to the entire gamut of thoughts, sensations, and emotions, be they painful or pleasurable.

Breath is not an action; it's a response, it responds to actions. When we decide to run up a hill, we don't stand there and breathe until we have enough air to make it up the hill. We start running. The air of the world, and our body's reflexes, without our having to ask, help us to accomplish what we have decided to do. Just like that. Such support. Such kindness. Such faithfulness. And how often do we stop and say 'thank you'?

The moment we stop and say 'thank you', and mean it, and feel it in our hearts, something finally stops. We stop doing. Breathing happens. We are simply being thankful.

When pressures mount, as they often do, stop utterly and completely and softly ask yourself, 'Who is breathing?'

And wait without waiting, until you know . . .

It's not you.

8 THE DECISION

———◆◆◆◆◆———

I

While Eva prepares dinner, I am in the living room holding a ceramic pot in my hands. 'Eva, tell me about the large brown pot by the window. It looks like it wasn't made. It looks more like it was grown.'

'My friend made that, Dorothea Chabert. We lost touch a long time ago. I don't even know if she's still alive.'

'Eva, why don't we find out?'

Eva did find out. She called a number she had penciled into an old address book. Eva's in her mid-eighties and never bothered with computers. It's a relief to be in her world for the days that I am every year, a world with few distractions, few interruptions, where long conversations happen over long meals, sitting at a beautifully set table with spoons, and plates, teacups and pitchers enjoyed by her family for generations. A world where time moves at its own pace. A world of hardback books, framed photographs, oil paintings, and pottery, a world you can feel and touch.

In Eva's little Fiat on the *Autobahn*, BMWs, Audis and Mercedes are passing us at alarming speed. 'Eva, tell me more about Dorothea.' 'Dorothea lives in Wolfsburg,' she says. 'She used to live in Wolfsburg Castle. Now she lives in the coach house beside the Castle. That's where we're going, to Wolfsburg Castle. She was part of an artist collective back in the Sixties called Schlosstrasse 8.

She taught ceramic art in a university for some years, I think in Braunschweig. She's better known in Japan than in Germany.'

'You can't be a prophet in your own city,' I say, 'sometimes not even in your own country,' realizing that's how it's been for me too.

Old wooden floors, huge wooden beams, large wooden worktables, and everywhere wooden shelves, like scaffolding, lined with pottery. A potter's paradise, I thought. 'Eva, I feel like I'm walking into a church.' 'Me too,' Eva says. Dorothea sits at her wheel, gazing out a large, open window. A soft, Vermeer-like light illuminates her calm, weather-worn face.

Hours pass in Dorothea's company, mesmerized by hundreds of bowls, vases, teapots, cups, containers, and large plates with glazes that look like galaxies. Being in Dorothea's studio is like being in a scholars' large, private library. I felt surrounded by a person's unpublished autobiography, written in clay.

In the twilight Dorothea's pottery sits within a numinous silence. As if she could read my thoughts, Dorothea says, 'I don't throw much anymore. I can't sit for very long because of my back. But I spend time looking at my wheel. On good days I used to feel God sitting right there in the centre of my wheel. On those days throwing a pot was like creation, like genesis, like a new world being born. I lived for those days, those meetings.'

Eva and I leave, each holding a simple cup in our hands, and Dorothea in our hearts.

II

Sitting in a room full of students, about to begin a workshop, I'm the opposite of nervous. I feel at home, in a place I know, a place full of warmth and comfort. Allowing the room to grow quiet on its own, listening for that poignant silence, I find myself thinking about Dorothea.

'I love pottery,' I say. 'It's the way it feels in my hands. One day I was in Italy. It was hot. I was thirsty. I spotted a water pump in a plaza. I primed the pump. Water spilled out. I squatted down, cupping my two hands together, filled my palms with cold water, and drank. I looked down at my wet hands and thought, two hands, the first bowl ever made.

'When I came here to Japan, I knew I had landed in my artistic home. Your country reveres pottery, constructs entire ceremonies around a tea bowl. The *chawan* is Japan's holy grail, a sacred vessel with a sacred purpose: to commune with nature, with people, and with life itself.

'Maybe that's why pottery feels so quintessentially human to me. We unearth ancient civilizations and what do we find? Pottery. Where there are people, there is pottery. The word human derives from the Latin, *humanus*, which derives from *humus*, which means earth. Human means "of the earth, or earthling". Look up synonyms for the word "earth" and you find: soil, loam, dirt, sod, clay.

'If we're made of clay, then maybe potters have something to teach us. Maybe if we study their creative process we might learn something about transformation, about how to change ourselves into something beautiful and useful.'

III

The metaphor has now been established for the workshop. It serves me, as you will see, as an outline for the workshop. Within the metaphor lies a sequence through which I can allow the work to unfold. It's a physical metaphor with metaphysical implications. That means while I am connecting the metaphor to their bodies, I am also connecting the metaphor to their lives, to what it means to be human. I've also set the stage for using my hands to do my work, for making physical contact with people. I have revealed a little about myself as a person; that I like pottery, that I've been to Italy, that I love Japan, and by revealing a bit about myself I am indirectly giving them permission to tell me about themselves.

My strategy is to begin big, to create breadth. What it means to be human. I don't want them reducing the work to their bodies. I want their attention on their lives, on how it feels to move through their days.

IV

'So where do potters begin? My friend, Filipe Ortega, an Apache potter from La Madera, New Mexico, who speaks four languages and has a Master's degree in theology, goes down to a nearby pit his relatives have used to extract clay since the early 1800s. It all begins there, in the ground. When Filipe calls the earth his mother, he's not being poetic. That's reality for him. He experiences the earth as his loving mother. It's his source of life, his source of support. What could be more obvious?

'Matter, from Latin *materia*, comes from *mater*, the word for mother. Physical life needs nurturance. Life cannot live without it. I'm a "matterist". I believe matter matters.

'But for a couple of thousand years many people have lived in cultures where the spiritual has been severed from the physical; the spiritual elevated, and the physical debased.

'If physical life is less valuable, the nurturers become less valued; the mothers, the caregivers, the nurses, the teachers, and the gardeners. Those of us who use our hands, our bodies to do our work, the manual workers, become deemed less worthy, of less worth, and thus are paid less, thought less of, less than those who make a living using their "higher" functions, who live in a more sophisticated world, an abstract and symbolic world.

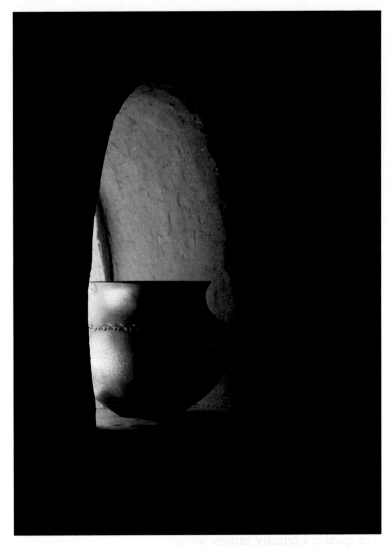

Fig. 19. Micaceous clay Apache bean pot by Filipe Ortega.

'This is one reason why it is important for me to be the kind of teacher I am, because first and foremost I am a nurturer, a person who cares for people. Education is wonderful but, alone, education is not enough for humans to grow. Education and nurturance together make people grow. My work is not about learning, it's about growing.

'Touch is an indispensable sense for nurturance. Infants cannot live without it. Certain primates spend up to 20 percent of their day in physical contact, grooming each other, huddling together when they are scared or need comfort, keeping themselves warm on cold nights, carrying their young on their backs as they go about their work. I am a manual worker, a male mother.

'The physical is holy. The senses are holy. The body possesses wisdom the mind will never understand. Coming to our senses, returning to the earth, remembering the mother of us all.'

V

'Before a potter begins to throw a pot, their clay must have a high degree of plasticity. That means it must be flexible, moist but not too moist, and strong but not dry or rigid. This is why potters have to wedge their clay. Once they get a homogenous distribution of tone through the clay, the clay "wakes up". The same is true for us.

'There are two ways of wedging clay. Some potters wedge clay into the shape of a ram's horn, but the Japanese often wedge clay into the shape of a conch shell, both spiraling forms. Embryologically, bones spiral themselves into existence, and then muscles spiral themselves in the opposite direction around the bones. It's a helical pattern. The heart itself is one spiraling muscle folded in on itself. The spiral is a primary pattern within us, and within the universe at large.'

I invite the group to huddle around my computer to watch a video of a master potter wedging clay. They look like little kids ready to watch some anime. It seems many of the students have never seen a person wedging clay. You can hear the occasional rising '*eeeehhhh* . . .' sound that Japanese make when they are surprised and impressed by something.

'Okay, let's begin to learn how to wedge our own clay.'

I demonstrate a movement on the floor, how a baby rolls over from its back to its front. I show them how it's possible to initiate this spiraling motion from the eyes and head, as well as from the solar plexus, or the knees, thighs, or pelvis, all creating spirals through the body.

I station my assistants around the room, placing them at the head of each student. They serve as a stimulus, something the baby wants to see, creating the impulse to initiate the spiraling motion from the eyes and head. I show them how to use their hands to assist the student in clearly initiating the movement from the eyes and head and ensuring that the body follows sequentially.

I've now begun to physicalize the metaphor. A moving idea is an idea that moves you. I sit down and watch. I watch both the Alexander trainees and teachers, and their students. Where needed, I help. People are animated and enjoying themselves. When I see that everyone has improved, I bring the group back together.

VI

'The clay is then patted into a sphere, another primary form within us and within the universe. A sphere is equally high, wide, and deep. This creates maximum volume, with minimum surface area. A sphere has neither sides, nor a top or a bottom. We have lots of sphere-like shapes within us, like our skull, rib basket, our pelvic basin, and lots of ball joints too, like our shoulders and hips. We're full of spheres, bowls and domes.'

The assistants and I go around the room showing them beautiful drawings of human spheres from *Albinus on Anatomy*. Then we go around gently enveloping all the heads, rib baskets, and pelvic basins in the room. Once I can see that everyone is sensing the roundness of their structure, I have them walk around the room.

'Is that how you usually feel when you walk down the street?' I ask. '*Zen zen jigau*, totally different,' several students say.

Everyone sits down, most of them look different, less collapsed, and less constricted.

VII

'The sphere of clay is then dropped onto the wheel, as close to centre as possible. But to get the clay truly centred, the potter almost always brings the clay up and down a few times, guiding it ever more finely onto centre. If you know the poem 'Burnt Norton', by T. S. Eliot, you cannot help but feel the connection between what the potter does and Eliot's "still point of the turning world". Eliot writes, " . . . at the still point, there the dance is."

'So let's bring the clay up and down. Humans get up and down in many ways, for all kinds of reasons. Buddhists and Muslims bow. Dancers plié. Aikidoists roll. We get up and down from chairs. Here we get up and down from *kotatsus* and futons.

'I happen to know that, in this room, we have a Zen priest, a professional ballet dancer, a couple aikidoists, and people that get up in the morning from their futons and down again at night after a hard day of work. Let's make four groups and do some rising and lowering. Go into the group you want and bring your clay up and down.'

I sit down and watch. I watch everyone. I do my best not to intervene unless absolutely necessary. And again, people are having a good time. For some unknown reason, the group of people bowing are by far having the most fun. They look reverent, and at any moment, about to break out in laughter. When it looks like a cou-

ple good waves of learning have happened, I invite people to finish
up and then sit down again.

VIII

'Now a great potter doesn't just bring their clay up and down in
any old way, they do it in a way where they become that still point
in the turning world. And we can learn to do that within ourselves
too. Alexander found a way into this. He called it a true and primary movement. He discerned that there was an inner movement,
an inner rising and lowering. This inner movement has a certain
look to it. It's effortless. It's smooth. It's light. It seems to happen
by itself. Let's look at another video, this time of a potter making
a bowl. The way the clay changes shape, the way it rises, widens,
and spreads looks a lot like Alexander's true and primary movement
feels.

'Watching a master potter turn a lump of clay into a bowl is
mesmerizing and magical. As you watch this make sure to imagine
the movement you are seeing actually happening in your body. See
what you are seeing kinaesthetically.'

Everyone is now ready and excited about experiencing this primary movement. Soon they will feel the effortless rising, the wet-
ness, the fluidity, the stability, the spreading, the still point in the
turning world. Before the first day of the workshop ends, everyone will have experienced themselves opening into a sense of space
unknown to them.

IX

'*Ohayo gosaimasu*,' I say to everyone, everyone bowing and answer-
ing together, '*Ohayo gosaimasu*.' 'Today my question is, What
about using our bowls? If they're going to last, don't they have to
be glazed and fired? Here's how I see it. The glaze is your person-
ality, your colour, your design, how you express yourself. Every

bowl is unique. There is no need to make them all look the same. I love that about Japan. When I go out to a good Japanese restaurant for dinner, I spend so much time just appreciating the beauty of the pottery. Nothing matches. No two pieces are the same. Just like people.

'And the firing? The firing is your life. Will you be able to withstand and survive the heat, the pressure of life, its demands, hardships, disappointments, and ordeals, without cracking irreparably? If you can, if you do make it through this trial by fire you will become useful, able to serve. And though you may, along the way, as I have, suffer cracking and chipping, and though you may even fall and shatter and have to glue yourself back together piece by piece, as I have, you will, with age, become beautiful.

'It's now time to discuss among yourselves, in small groups, what situations in your life are currently stressful. It may be a situation at work, dealing with deadlines, with bossy bosses. It may be relating with your partner, or your children, or your parents. It might be the pressure of performance. But whatever the situation, take time now, find the people in the room who can help you set up the stressful situation you find yourself in, and let's enter the fire together.'

The stage is now set for the second day of class, for applying the work into their lives.

Scenes are enacted; an aging daughter caring for an aging parent, a teacher unable to motivate her students, an analyst stuck behind a computer all day, a singer with performance anxiety, a therapist listening to a suicidal client, a physical therapist having to help a stroke patient up from a wheelchair and into a bed. These are the kinds of situations that inspire me. The tough ones.

X

It's time to bring the workshop to a close, always a delicate moment, like arriving at the last line of a poem.

'You are the clay. You are the material with which you have to work. You are the potter. You are the bowl. You are the person who shapes yourself. You are the person who has the potential to open yourself. You are the one who can make yourself beautiful, and useful.

'And it is you who must, ultimately, ask the question and make the decision. With what do I wish to fill myself?'

The room is utterly silent. We sit in that silence together for a long time, in a circle that suddenly looks to me like one big bowl. I bow, thanking my translator of 27 years, my organized organizer, my dedicated trainees, and all the open-hearted students. And silently, so only I can hear, I thank my teachers.

I am filled with gratitude. Yes, I think to myself, that's my decision.

Part II

STUDENT-CENTRED TEACHING

To be means to be with other people. Existence is coexistence.[14]

Rabbi Abraham Joshua Heschel

Introduction:

in every person

Having been a teacher for 55 years, having studied with many teachers, and having trained hundreds of teachers, three teaching temperaments or orientations present themselves: teachers predominately centred around ideas, principles, and theories, teachers centred around skill, method, and technique, and teachers centred around their students.

And yes, this is overly simplistic. Teachers seem to possess a dominant *modus operandi*, their most developed and most used, as well as a 'best supporting' mode, the mode most successfully interwoven with and supportive of the dominant mode. And a teacher has a latent potential mode, their least actualized mode. When a teacher's latent mode is actualized and integrated into their work, it transforms an already good teacher into an often masterful teacher.

By way of explaining what I mean, I wish to honour my Alexander mentors: Marjorie Barstow (Marj), Richard M. Gummere Jr. (Buzz), Catherine Wielopolska (Kitty), Elisabeth Walker, and Erika Whitaker, all students of F. M. Alexander.

Kitty, Buzz, and Erika were primarily idea-centred teachers, all very student-centred as well. Actually, Buzz and Erika did not consider themselves teachers. Buzz was happy in the role of an advisor or counselor, and in our school's case, as philosopher/historian-in-residence. Erika felt her role to be that of an experienced friend who engaged her students in conversation. They enjoyed thinking about Alexander's work and its implications. What did John

Dewey mean when he said that Alexander's work bears the same relation to education that education bears to all other human activities? What is the Alexander Technique: a technique, a method, a study, a practice, or a way of life? Was it an art or a science? In which university department did it belong; philosophy, physical education, the performing arts, psychology, or theology, and why or why not? Could people improve, not just physically, but morally from long-term study of the technique, as John Dewey postulated? Or, when Alexander said, 'Bring me a thief and I'll make him a better thief; bring me a saint and I'll make him a better saint,' did he imply that, ultimately, how we made good use of our good use was up to us? Countless hours over dinners, in cars, in trains, between classes, and at parties I mused upon Alexander's work with people who trained with and knew Alexander well.

Kitty had a strong mystical bent and would talk to me about how Alexander's ideas paralleled ideas found in the work of Gurdjieff, Delsarte, Dalcroze and Steiner. She'd talk about the similarities between Alexander's ideas and Dr. Bates' ideas about the eyes, or Dr. Stough's ideas about breathing. She was more intuitive than intellectual, excited about the work, always on the cusp of a new discovery. At the same time, Kitty always had a crock of hot soup and fresh bread and butter sitting out, ready for her poor and hungry dance students.

Interestingly, neither Buzz, nor Erika, nor Kitty were confident using their hands. None of them were somatically oriented.

In stark contrast, Marjorie Barstow was a technique-centred teacher. To my eye, her passion was in perfecting her technique. She was profoundly physical. Like me, she had been a gymnast and a modern dancer and, unlike me, she rode horses and had trained some world famous quarter horses. Marj moved well. She could see, assess, and access fine coordination, be it in a person or a horse.

When I first began working with Marj, well before her osteoporosis set in, I remember one sunny summer day in downtown Lincoln, Nebraska, walking behind Marj as she walked down O Street in her dungaree jacket, blue jeans, and cowgirl boots. Marj's body and back looked like it belonged to a well coordinated 35-year-old rancher. From behind her no one would have guessed that back and body belonged to a weather worn 76-year-old woman.

Marj loved using her hands. She used them beautifully and consciously all day long, whether she was teaching, cleaning her house, cooking dinner, or raking leaves.

We were there for her to work on her skill. She was the potter. She had to throw a lot of pots, every day, and we were her clay. She put us on her wheel, effortlessly gliding us up and opening us out. Enthralled, I watched Marj throw one stunning pot after another, hour after hour, day after day, year after year, for many, many years. I loved her hands and vowed not to quit until I had hands as skilled and refined as hers.

As for her students, well, she loved observing us, all the wild things we did, dancing, singing, acting, aikido, tai chi, juggling, anything and everything. For her, out there in Lincoln, Nebraska, we were a good source of entertainment. She enjoyed watching how we did what we did and then figuring out how to refine and empower everything we did, always without using force. She liked us, but always from a distance. She was an artist, a maestro, married to her work.

Elisabeth Walker was a student-centred teacher. In all the years I watched her teach not once did I see her in conflict with a student, not once did I see her or hear her make a student feel bad about themselves. A mother of five children, she was a born nurturer. She loved people. And people, in turn, loved her. She was the epitome of graciousness. Elisabeth's intellectual and somatic skills were also highly developed. She was a solid, well-rounded teacher.

To be honest, I am uncertain as to my dominant, supporting, and latent potential modes. If I had to guess I would say in my early years as an Alexander teacher I was strongly idea-oriented. That led me into a long period devoted to developing my teaching skills and sensibilities; tactile, kinetic, kinaesthetic, visual, auditory, vocal, and linguistic. It wasn't until life forced me to stop, until I saw my way through a long, dark night into the light of day, that I began, truly, to become a student-centred teacher.

Now, though I remain keen on ideas and on the acquisition of skill, it is people who intrigue me, who challenge me, who move me, and who enlighten me.

As fate would have it, I have had and continue to have a blessed career as a teacher. I began helping people to move well at the age of eleven, when the director of Willow Grove Day Camp, knowing not what to do with me, my being your classic ADHD kid, handed me over to Barbara Bronstein, the swimming instructor, who had me begin each day swimming 20 laps. This calmed me down and cleared my mind. The rest of the day I spent teaching little kids how to swim. They'd hold on to the side of the pool and I'd gently lengthen their legs, guiding their small feet down into the water so as not to over-splash, helping them find their rhythm. I'd softly rotate their little hips so their whole bodies rotated easily from side to side. I'd show them how to turn their heads to breathe by resting their skulls in the water, leaving their necks long and simply rotating their heads to the side, just enough to get their mouths out of the water.

When I wasn't teaching swimming I was teaching kids how to dive head first into the water. I'd get the little ones who thought they were diving when what they were really doing was lifting their arms up over their heads, putting their palms together, tucking their chins into their chests, pointing their fingers toward the water, closing their eyes, and then jumping in, feet first.

I'd have them stand at the edge of the pool. Then I'd have them squat down onto their heels. Instead of having them put their arms over their heads, I'd have them point their fingers straight down into the water. Ever so lightly I would lead their fingers toward the water with one hand while gently tilting their heads forward with my other hand, then I'd quickly take my hand that was leading their fingers, place it under their pelvis, give a little upward suggestion while still gently leading their heads toward the water, and *voilà*, in they'd go, rolling forward into the water, head first.

After many, many successes, little by little I'd have them squat a tiny bit less deeply, and before long they could dive into the water from a stand.

At twelve I became a gymnast, and that is what I lived and breathed for eight years. Again, camp directors kept me out of trouble by having me teach kids, which I did for ten years.

By the time I entered my first Alexander teacher training program, at 23, I was comfortable using my hands on day one. I had my problems, for sure, but nervousness around using my hands was not one of them.

Ballet pas de deux classes, tai chi push hand classes, aikido classes, and tango classes followed, continuous training using my hands, bringing people into balance, or out of balance, as the situation called for, both requiring similar tactual sensitivity.

At 32, perhaps prematurely, I began training Alexander teachers. I knew I had stepped into a suit way too big for me. I figured I'd just have to grow into it. After tripping over my own two feet a good bit, I did grow into it, though honestly, I am still dissatisfied with my ability when it comes to training teachers.

People began asking me to teach in other countries. Wherever I was invited, I went. Thirty years, four continents and 25 countries later, I am still traveling and teaching, using my hands, enabling people to move more gracefully through the lives they are living. This has been a great pleasure and privilege.

The stories that follow are true. Names and minor details have been changed as a way of protecting people's privacy. Some of these meetings, open-hearted encounters, conversations, sessions, lessons, took place 40 years ago, some just this year.

Elie Wiesel writes, 'We must not see *any* person as an abstraction. Instead, we must see in every person a universe with its own secrets, with its own treasures, with its own sources of anguish, and with some measure of triumph.'[15]

Here I share with you universes, and within them, secrets, treasures, anguish, and triumphs.

LIKING PEOPLE

1 ON LEVEL GROUND

—•◦•◦•—

'Many people have asked me how, as a teacher, I get people to trust me so quickly and deeply. Being a movement educator, I often use my hands when I work, and because I do not have much time with a person, knowing how to establish almost immediate trust is essential to my working effectively.

'As doctors you are often in a similar position. Often, you do not have much time with a patient and you want your patients to trust you.

'Establishing trust has less to do with what you say to a person, or even what you do. Establishing trust has mostly to do with how you are being within yourself when you are with a person.

'Once, after a class, I was surprised by how much warmth I felt directed toward me from everyone in the group. Innocently, I asked my friend, "Why do people like me so much?" "Bruce, it is so simple. It's because you like them."

'For me, liking people is natural. There is no technique. I am a person who likes people. I don't know if you can teach a person how to like people. I really don't know. But maybe it is possible.

'Being a person in a position of authority, or being a person with great skill, does not guarantee trust or respect. What makes a person feel close to you is meeting them, as equals, on common ground.

'One day, after I had taught for 21 days, from morning to night, and I am not Japanese, I finally had one day off. It was a sunny day.

I felt free. I decided to buy some small presents for my wife and kids. Walking down the street, a young man who looks like he's about 20 comes up to me, smiles, and says, "Don't I know you?" "I'm sorry. I don't think so," I say. "You look so familiar," he says. I walk for another ten steps and a small, old lady whom I did not know stops me, looks directly into my eyes and says, "I know you, I am sure I know you, but for the life of me I cannot remember from where," she says. "I just have one of those faces. Maybe it's because I look like Paul Simon," I say smiling. She looked at me for a long time. I wished her well and continued my walk when, 30 seconds later, another man, about my age, who actually looked a lot like me, stops me and asks me my name and where I am from. "My name is Bruce, Bruce Fertman. I live in Philadelphia," I say. "No, I don't know you. But I feel like I know you." Without thinking I say, "We do know each other. We've just never met before."'

'That day it seemed everyone knew me, and I knew everyone. That never happened to me quite like that again, but on that day it happened.'

'Personally, I do not believe in reincarnation, but I like something His Holiness the Dalai Lama once said. He said we have all been reborn so many times that everyone we meet has already been our mother, our father, our husband, our wife, our daughter, our son, and our best friend. I like to imagine myself not only as a white male but as someone who has already been male and female, Black and Latino, Asian and Aborigine, as someone who has been lesbian and bisexual, gay and transgender, someone who has been a Muslim, Hindu, Christian and Jew, a Buddhist and a Sikh, who has been rich and poor, married and unmarried, physically able and physically challenged.

'I do my best to see a person in this light when I meet them. I see them as a member of my family. By virtue of being human they are related to me and I am to them.

'People feel this immediately. And sometimes, in that one moment, a deep trust is established. In that one moment, the student or the stranger on the street knows they are safe with me, that I care about them, that I see them, that I am ready and happy to give them my attention and my time.

'Teaching is an art, medicine is too. They are social arts.

'Medical schools turn people into doctors. In our brief but important time together let's consider how we can turn doctors back into plain people who engender immediate trust from their patients. And let's have fun doing it,' I say to a room full of people, all of whom look so familiar to me.

2 A LITTLE LIGHTNESS

Mr. Yamamoto has had a long day.

Finally finished, he gets on his bicycle and winds his way through narrow streets lined with old, dusty shops and wood weathered houses. It's winter, 6:30 pm and already dark. Heavy, white snowflakes fall in slow motion through an indigo sky, the way they have in Kyoto for 1,400 years.

Mr. Yamamoto emerges from the back streets of Old Kyoto and into what looks like another world, wide avenues full of vertical neon signs, large LED advertising screens, high-rise financial institutions, and upscale department stores. He pulls in front of a Seven Eleven, grabs a bento and a box of butter cookies to share during the break, gets back on his bike and realizes he's late.

Mr. Yamamoto is a 50-year-old high school math teacher who dreams of retiring. Inside his beat up leather briefcase, which now rests, seemingly exhausted, in his bicycle basket, are his students' math exams, which he will be grading late into the night, because this evening he will take a class he wants to take, a class for himself.

Mr. Yamamoto is hoping to learn more about his body. He wants to have more energy. He wants to have some fun, do something good for himself. At the suggestion of a friend, against his better judgement, he signs up for a series of classes in the Alexander Technique.

About twelve students have gathered, men and women, old and young, people for the most part who just want to feel more alive, a bit lighter, a little happier.

Tonight I've been working with the students doing things they have to do at work, things they don't like doing. I worked with a man who receives phone calls from disgruntled customers complaining about what they just bought and wish to return. I worked with a woman scrubbing a wooden floor on her hands and knees. I worked with a man who has to listen to his boss yelling at him first thing in the morning.

It's Mr. Yamamoto's turn. He unsnaps his briefcase and slides out his stack of ungraded exams. He walks over to a desk in the corner of the room, sits down behind the desk, drops the pile of papers onto the desk, pulls out a pencil from his shirt pocket, lets out a big sigh, and begins.

I just watch, feeling how he feels, sensing what's happening throughout my entire body as I see his entire body. Under the table I can see that his feet and legs are turned in, especially his left leg. His pelvis is rolling back. His stomach is tight. His chest is sunken. His head is dropped and tilted to the left. His body looks like it's crying, but Mr. Yamamoto is not crying. Then I see it and feel it: silent, desperate resignation.

Mr. Yamamoto scribbles something onto the first exam. 'How did your student do,' I ask?' 'D. Not good.' Mr. Yamamoto continues. C. D. C+. F. He's shaking his head. He's aging right before my eyes.

'Mr. Yamamoto (that's what everyone calls him), how do you feel about my helping you a little?' '*Onegaishimasu*,' he says, bowing slightly. 'Please help me.' I walk behind him, softly place my hands, one on either side of his neck, and gently guide his head back on top of his body. His body rises up like a man under water who's finally coming up for air. His chest swells, his whole body expands reflexively in every direction. '*Zen, zen chigau, waaaaa*,' Mr. Yamamoto says with a look of ecstasy on his face. Everyone laughs. I can feel how much everyone likes him.

'Okay, Mr. Yamamoto, begin grading your papers and let's see what happens.'

B. Everyone smiles, but not Mr. Yamamoto. B+. *Eeeeeeeh!?*, a rising sound heard when Japanese people are pleasantly surprised. More smiles and some laughter, but not from Mr. Yamamoto.

A. A. A+. A. Now everyone's literally rolling on the floor laughing uncontrollably. It's irrepressible. Yet Mr. Yamamoto remains still and expressionless. I'm not sure what he's feeling. I'm doing my best to stick with him, but the unbridled laughter in the room is too contagious. I lose it.

And suddenly so does Mr. Yamamoto. He's laughing so hard tears are rolling down his cheeks. 'Maybe those crazy Buddhists are right,' Mr. Yamamoto says. 'Maybe the world is nothing but one big mirror.'

'On that note, let's finish,' I say. Quickly everyone sits in a circle on the floor, kneeling in *seiza*, and bows deeply. Still smiling from ear to ear, we loudly exclaim, '*Doumo arigatou gosaimashita*.' Thank you very, very much. We're thankful to be together, thankful to be learning, thankful for a little lightness in our lives, thankful for Mr. Yamamoto.

Mr. Yamamoto throws his scarf around his neck, tosses his briefcase into the basket, and hops onto his bike. The crisp night air fills his lungs. The snow looks whiter. It's swirling. It's falling up.

3 IN BLIND DAYLIGHT

Below, in a dingy subway station, sitting cross-legged on a blue blanket, her golden hair hangs straight and long down her back. Beside her lies a black labrador, his chin resting upon his crisscrossed paws. Head tilting back, gazing out of her large black sunglasses, guitar in her lap, she's singing a song I don't know. Albums and tapes sit next to a small basket filled mostly with coins and a few one-dollar bills.

Her song ends. The dog sits up. Putting a dollar in her basket, though at the time I was living on a meager, self-allotted $25 a week allowance, I ask her who wrote that song. She says she did. She asks me what I do. 'I dance with a modern dance company, study tai chi, and I'm beginning to teach something called the Alexander Technique,' I say.

'I've heard of the Alexander Technique. I'd love to study. My voice gets tired after about an hour, my back too,' she says. I ask her where she lives. 'In Germantown.' 'Me too. I'd be happy to give you a lesson in exchange for one of your albums,' I say. 'That's a deal,' she says, handing me an album and a tape.

Ellen rings the doorbell right on time. 'Up the steps and straight back through the kitchen,' I say. 'Up the steps and straight back through the kitchen,' she says to her dog. Her dog leads the way, Ellen follows, and I follow Ellen. Watching her walk up the steps I see she's exceptionally upright but quite stiff along her entire spine. I later find out her stiffness came, in part, from years spent walking

with a stick and bumping into side mirrors of big trucks and such –
things her dog now sees well ahead of time and avoids.

After a brief introduction as to what Alexander's work is about, I
suggest we begin simply with her sitting back in a chair. I encourage her to slowly and softly sink into a comfortable slump. 'Ellen,' I
say, 'slumping and uprightness are not two different positions, one
wrong and one right. Together they make up a range of motion,
and emotion, a continuum upon which you can learn to slide up
and down easily and comfortably.' We spend a good bit of time on
this until her rigidity, which feels like anxiety under my hands, is
gone.

'Ellen,' I say, for purely selfish reasons, 'sing me a song.' Smiling, her smile large and expressive, she says, 'I won't be needing
my guitar for this one . . .'

> *I see trees of green, red roses too. I see them bloom, for me and you.*
> *And I think to myself, what a wonderful world.*
> *I see skies of blue, and clouds of white. The bright blessed day,*
> *the dark sacred night. And I think to myself, what a wonder-*
> *ful world.*
> *The colours of the rainbow, so pretty in the sky, are also on the*
> *faces of people going by.*
> *I see friends shaking hands, saying, 'How do you do?' They're*
> *really saying, 'I love you.'*
> *I hear babies cry, I watch them grow. They'll learn much more, than*
> *I'll ever know. And I think to myself, what a wonderful world.*[16]

She finishes. I ask her how that felt. 'More comfortable,' she
says. 'I could hear my voice sounding smoother, less raspy. I could
see everything more clearly.' Later I learn Ellen inherited retini-
tis pigmentosa and could see well until she was six years old, when

her sight began to fail. By the time she was twelve she was legally blind, as opposed to illegally blind, she used to say.

'Ellen, how do you feel, not in your body but as a person, just as a person inside yourself?,' I ask. 'I feel less guarded, like there was a wall around me and now there isn't. I didn't know it was there. Yeah, less alone, I feel less alone,' she says. 'Great. That's it for today. Call me if you want to continue,' I say.

The next day she calls. 'Bruce, after the lesson I went to the park and sat on a park bench where I often sit and play. I sat down and I didn't feel like playing so I didn't. It was enough just to sit in the warm sunlight and feel myself in the world without my "wall". A man came over, asked if he could sit down on the bench next to me. First time that ever happened! You know, I sing as a way of reaching out to people. And here I was reaching out to nobody and somebody walks right up and sits down next to me. We talked a lot and for a long time, about real things. It was effortless. Bruce, I'd like to study more,' she says. 'Sure, just pay me what you can afford. I'm a new teacher. I need the practice,' I say.

Ellen and I worked together for two years. At some point she wanted to learn tai chi ch'uan. She said she couldn't figure out how to study it because she couldn't see it. She heard that it was beautiful and she liked the philosophy behind it. 'Sounds like Alexander Technique in motion,' she says. 'That's how it feels to me, and yes, I'd be happy to teach you tai chi,' I say.

Through touch and language I led her through every little movement, over and over again. Her movement memory was great. Ellen loved my touch. 'You know, people want to help me all the time. Well-meaning, they grab my arm and pull me with one hand while pushing me with the other. They squeeze me, jerk me, and press me down to stop me. But you do almost nothing. Your touch is so soft, and I know exactly what you want me to do and where you want me to go,' she says. 'I have good teachers,' I say.

Guiding her with my hands, I would do the form behind her, like some benevolent shadow, like one of those angels in Wim Wenders' *Wings of Desire*. Though I was behind her, she followed me as I followed her.

Balance was not an issue for Ellen. She had plenty of practice balancing without seeing. She knew where the ground was through her feet. Her vestibular balance must have been good. It looked like her hearing helped her balance as well. She seemed to know the precise angle from which a sound was coming.

Most challenging was getting Ellen's form spatially accurate. I began by getting her to imagine herself inside of a large cube. I got her to sense front, and back, and sides, the front diagonals, and the back diagonals, all the corners of the cube, and of course the top and the bottom. Once the cube was firmly in place, we began trimming off the edges of the cube until, there she was, moving clearly and calmly within an invisible sphere.

Ellen came to know, kinaesthetically, exactly how far, exactly how many degrees her hip joints had to rotate in their sockets for hundreds of little movements in the tai chi form. She applied this same sensitivity to her ankles and knees, to her wrists, elbows and shoulders, to her spine and head. Each joint became a compass.

Ellen taught me how to live like a blind man who just happens to be able to see. I taught Ellen how to see kinaesthetically. The more the senses open to the world, the more the world opens to us. And the walls they come a-tumbling down.

4 SUNG-HO

It may be beyond my area of expertise. It may be foolish, even unprofessional, even unethical. It may be sheer chutzpah, or profound innocence, or it may not be any of these.

Sung-ho walks into my apartment studio in downtown Seoul. He clearly has what I like to call an unconventional nervous system, or an exceptional structure.

Having only known Sung-ho for two days, he already feels like a friend. We spent a night together jammed into a packed subway car, talking politics, making our way down crowded streets into the heart of a peaceful, passionate, and packed protest with 1.7 million other people.

No matter the circumstances, Sung-ho just keeps up. He doesn't complain. In fact, he directs his attention toward others, making sure everyone's comfortable.

He thinks his English is terrible. 'I am eternally grateful to anyone who can speak any English, Sung-ho. I understand everything you are saying.' 'I want to ask you something,' Sung-ho says. 'In America, what do you call people who are disabled?' 'We call them physically challenged. Calling a person disabled sums them up as people who are not able to function properly. We prefer describing their situation. A physically challenged person is a person who is challenged physically. When I watch people like you, I see an athlete, a person who is training for an Olympic event called everyday life.' 'I like that,' Sung-ho says.

Sung-ho explains his situation to me. 'I'm in pain most of the time. My left hip hurts almost continually. I can't lift my right hand past my shoulder. I can't turn my head at all. My spine doesn't move. It's in a permanent C-shape. Whenever, by mistake, I go outside of my small range of motion it's really painful. I'm always working hard to move and when I sit down and relax my body hurts even more, so I keep my muscles tight. But I'm used to it. It's been this way since I was a kid.'

Later I find out Sung-ho, when he was 15, was diagnosed with ankylosing spondylitis, an inflammatory disease that, for reasons unknown, mostly afflicts young men. Over time this extreme form of arthritis causes the spine to fuse, making the spine increasingly immobile. Ankylosing spondylitis is incurable.

'Sung-ho, let me see what you do when you relax.' I watch as he presses his shoulder girdle down onto his upper ribs and pushes his chest in. 'Sung-ho, that hurts because that is not relaxing, but we will get to that later. Right now show me how much you can move your head without pain. With your head say yes, no, and maybe,' I say, demonstrating. He does. He moves his head about one inch in every direction, but that one inch is accomplished by ever so slight bending or rotating movements initiated down around his rib cage. The relationship of his head to his neck is frozen like a block of ice. 'Good. I want to see you move. I'd like you to get up and walk to the closet, put on your coat, then take it off, hang it back up, walk back here, and sit down.' I just watch, kinaesthetically empathizing more than I am analysing. This familiar aching feeling settles over me, a feeling I often feel when working with physically challenged people, this feeling of guilt. Why them and why not me?

'You get around,' I say. 'I make myself do everything,' Sung-ho says. 'An athlete,' I say.

'Okay, Sung-ho. I am going to teach you something that helps me a lot. It may sound strange, and it's not scientific, but it allows me to move more easily and comfortably. All it takes is a playful imagination and some practice. Are you willing to try?' 'Sure,' Sung-ho says.

'I like to think of myself as having two bodies, a being body and a doing body. The being body is my inner body and my doing body is my outer body. My outer body is substantial and made of muscle. But inside that body is a body that has no substance. It's weightless. It moves like a gentle wind, like a soft breeze. It moves effortlessly. It's comfortable, and it's never in pain. The inner body has no bones. It's just space. Sometimes it feels like a friendly ghost body. Deep within you it flies freely.

'What I like to imagine is that my inner body, my being body, my ghost body, moves my doing body from the inside out. I imagine that my inner body is moving and my outer body just comes along with it. The outer body doesn't do anything, just as your clothes don't move by themselves. They are moved by your body. So your outer body doesn't do anything by itself. It is moved by your inner body.' Sung-ho seems to like the idea. He's smiling.

'Sung-ho, can you just sit here now, close your eyes and imagine that who you really are is your inner body and not your outer body?' I watch him. I can see he's living inside of his imagination and that is where I want him to be. 'Sung-ho, that is closer to real relaxation.'

'Okay, here is a little way of practising shifting from your outer body to your inner body. Imagine you have a fly buzzing around your face and you want to brush it away. Let your hand just fly up and move the fly away.' 'That's easy,' Sung-ho says. 'Is it comfortable,' I ask? 'Very.' 'That's your inner body flying around and your outer body just coming along with it. Now brush the fly away by moving your outer body. What's that feel like?' I ask. 'That's harder, heavier, and slower.'

'Right. I think you move yourself around from your outer body. And I think, with practice, you could learn to move yourself around with your inner body.

'Okay, Sung-ho. Let's go back to saying "yes", "no", "maybe", with your head, but this time let your inner body, your inner head, do the moving and let your outer body, your outer head, just go with it.'

I watch. I think I see some actual head movement, but I'm not sure. 'How does that feel?', I ask. 'It's different, but I can't say how,' Sung-ho says. 'Was it comfortable?', I ask. 'Comfortable,' Sung-ho says.

'Okay. Let's play with something else. Touch the tip of your nose.' I watch and see that Sung-ho does that from his inner body. 'That's your inner body,' I say. 'I can feel that,' Sung-ho says.

'Imagine the tip of your nose is a small, very high quality calligraphy brush and write your name in the air with your calligraphy brush.' He does. I see that the tentativeness is completely gone and now Sung-ho is actually, however minutely, moving his head through rotational and pivotal movement in his upper cervical vertebrae. 'How's that,' I ask? 'It's wonderful,' Sung-ho says. 'That's your imagination and your inner body moving your outer body.' Sung-ho nods 'yes' even more freely, without knowing it.

'Sung-ho, do you have memories of yourself and of your body before you developed this condition?', I ask. 'Yes, I do.' 'Can you remember how old you were when you were super attracted, sexually attracted, to a girl? How old were you?' I ask. 'I was twelve,' Sung-ho says. 'What was her name?' 'Mi Kyung,' Sung-ho says, smiling from ear to ear. 'Okay, Sung-ho. I want your inner body to be twelve years old. You are totally in love with Mi Kyung. Now write her name with your calligraphy brush.'

I watch and see Sung-ho move his head three times as far in every direction. 'Wow!' Sung-ho says. 'Wow is right,' I say. 'You were so in love when you wrote Mi Kyung's name you forgot to be afraid to move your head.'

'Okay, let's stand up and walk around.' I watch Sung-ho stand up. He's tight. He's cringing. 'My left hip hurts a lot when I get up, especially after sitting for a long time,' Sung-ho says. 'I see that, but I also see that your ankles, knees and hips have a lot of flexion. I noticed that last night watching you go up steps. Your legs are strong. Let's walk around.'

Sung-ho throws his pelvis way forward and under his body because if he brought his pelvis back and up on top of his legs, he'd be looking straight down at the ground. When he walks his feet are far apart and quite turned out. His knees hardly flex. Yet, he walks faster than I do, almost as if he were in a race.

'Sung-ho, I know you can flex your knees more than that because you do when you get up and down from a chair, and when you go up and down steps. So let's imagine that your outer legs are just like a pair of super baggy pants, and let your inner legs move around inside your baggy pants. There's plenty of room in there. And pretend you are on vacation and there's nothing you have to do. The weather is warm, and you have all the time in the world.'

Clearly, Sung-ho has a powerful imagination and somehow he's able to connect his imagination to his kinaesthetic sense, an ability that takes many people a while to learn. 'How's that, Sung-ho?'

'It fun. And much easier. And comfortable,' Sung-ho says.

'I'm so glad, Sung-ho. We are going to stop now because you have some real tools to play with. You've got your very powerful imagination, and you have your very free inner body.' He's smiling. He's moved, holding back tears.

For a second the question flashes through my mind: Was that an Alexander lesson or not? Maybe. Maybe not. 'And maybe it doesn't matter,' I hear a voice inside me saying.

'Hey, Sung-ho. I finish teaching at ten tonight. As your wife is in my class, how about we all meet up after class and go out for a beer?' Sung-ho lights up and says, 'I know a place right around the corner that has Guinness on draft. Do you like Guinness?' 'A lot, especially when it's fresh. See you tonight.'

I watch Sung-ho get his coat. His movements are less jerky, longer, smoother. That aching feeling returns and I wonder, 'If I had Sung-ho's body, would I be able to adapt as gracefully to life as Sung-ho?'

Grace, it's not about how we look, or how we move. It's about who we are.

LISTENING TO PEOPLE

1 ALL THE TIME IN THE WORLD

It was the end of class. There were a few minutes left. I asked if anyone had any questions. Mizuho asked me how I listen to a student.

As usual, I sat there silently for about 20 seconds, waiting for an honest answer to arise.

'Let me tell you how my father, at the end of his life, listened to people. He'd sit down with someone and ask him or her, "How are you?" And he'd really mean it. My dad's ego died a couple of years before he did. His life no longer circled around itself.

'His friend, and it seemed everyone was his friend, whether he knew them or not, would talk about themselves, and when they finished – only when they had finished – my dad would ask them a question. "What was that like?" And then the person would talk. "And then what happened?", my dad would ask. And then the person would talk. "And how did that make you feel?"

'His friend would continue, sometimes for a long time. Ironically, now that my dad had so little time left, he lived as if he had all the time in the world.

'Five days before my dad died he was in the Intensive Care Unit. He was having a lot of trouble breathing. A nurse comes in and my father asks, "How are you?" She tells my dad, "To be honest, I'm exhausted. Last night I went to night school after a ten-hour shift. My daughter was up most of the night with an earache. This morning at six I grabbed a cup of coffee and a donut, got on the

bus and punched into work at seven for another ten-hour shift."
My dad asked, "How was your daughter in the morning?" And
then, "What are you studying in night school?" And then, "You're
amazing. I'm sure that will pay off in the long run for you and
your daughter." And then, "How old is your daughter? What's her
name?"'

'As the nurse is about to leave, my dad thanks her for being so
kind to him.

'Mizuho, when I am teaching well, I listen the way my dad listened. Sometimes when I am alone, sitting at a café, I feel he is still
asking me how I am, still sitting there across from me at the table,
still listening as if he had all the time in the world.'

2 THE LETTER

━━━●━◆━●━━━

Yuki's a quiet young woman. She's larger than most Japanese women, yet manages to move through the world unseen. Her eyes look almost hot, as if they're burning inside. Sitting there in class, suddenly without notice, her eyes fill with tears, which she then holds back. I can't be sure, but it looks like she's hurting inside.

Yuki asks if she can read a letter, a letter from her sister. 'Of course,' I say. I'm wondering why and, as if she can hear my question, she tells me. 'My sister is in a hospital. She's mentally unbalanced. She writes me letters that are very disturbing. They scare me. When I read them I can't move. I can hardly breathe.'

'It sounds like you like your sister very much,' I say. 'I do,' Yuki says. 'And I feel terrible because I don't know how to help her.'

'Read your sister's letter. I'd like you to read it out loud if that is okay with you.' Yuki nods. 'I want you to read a few sentences to us, and then read them again to yourself. And just continue like that for a while.' Yuki begins.

I don't understand Japanese. I have no idea what Yuki is reading. My translator has stopped translating. I look around. Everyone is riveted. I don't need to know what is being read. In fact, it's better if I don't. I'm just watching my person.

Yuki looks like she's been punched in the stomach. The hand holding the letter is trembling. Her voice sounds strange, guttural, sounds that don't sound Japanese. When Yuki reads to herself, nothing changes. It's just as painful. She can hardly move, hardly breathe.

All the while I've been sitting next to Yuki, beside her and slightly behind her, in her blind spot. That's where I often am when I work with my students, beside them and behind them. I can almost appear and disappear at will.

Reappearing, I place my hand on top of Yuki's hand, the hand holding the letter, and softly guide her hand down so that it and the letter can rest in her lap. 'Yuki, I see what you are doing. This won't be difficult. I'd like to use my hands to help you if that's okay?' I ask. She nods.

Over the next five minutes I help Yuki to effortlessly uncoil. Little by little, from the bottom up, I get Yuki's back resting against the back of her chair. I help her legs to un-brace. Her stomach relaxes. Her chest begins to fill out. She's breathing fully and peacefully. Her head floats back on top of her spine as if by itself.

'Yuki, the chair is giving you its support and protection,' I say. 'It wants you to rest.' I see the last remnant of tension leave Yuki's face. I put my hand under Yuki's hand and gently raise her hand and with it the letter. 'Yuki, continue sensing the support from the chair. Remain in full contact with the chair and read.' Yuki's voice is soft and clear. When she stops and reads to herself, she's calm, calmer than I've ever seen her.

'How are you doing Yuki-san?'

'I'm with my sister. But I am over here and she is over there. I can't help her if I go over there. I can only help her from here where I am,' she says.

There's nothing for me to add. I look into those eyes, no longer red and burning, but warm, soft and loving.

3 THE TANGO LESSON

It was like giving a lesson to Pablo Veron and Geraldine Rojas in *Assassination Tango*. They were perfect. They were gorgeous. My job was to watch them, to find a way I could be of help to them, but instead I sat there transfixed by how they moved. It wasn't just how they moved, it was how they became the music, how they were the music. They danced together until the end of the song. Spellbound, I knew I had to say something, had to do something. But what!

'What do you perceive as your problem?' I asked.

Gabriel begins. 'Of course, I love dancing with Maria. We have been partners for years. But there are moments when I feel resistance. Instead of the door being wide open and my simply being able to walk in, I begin to feel as if I have to open the door to walk in. The door opens easily, this is true, but still, I have to open it. It keeps me from being totally free.'

'Maria, how about you? What happens inside of you?'

'I love dancing with Gabriel too. I've never had a dance partner like him, and probably never will again. It's very hard to explain. When it is all working Gabriel doesn't really feel like a person. It feels like I am dancing with a force of nature, as if I were being moved by the wind. I feel like I am outside in a vast space. I feel like I am who I was meant to be. When it's not all working, I feel Gabriel asking me to do something. It's almost always clear and articulate, and easy to follow, but there is now a split, a separation.

He asks and I have to answer. He leads and I have to follow. I'm sorry. I can't really explain it.'

'No, you're painting a good picture. It says a lot. I'd like both of you to begin dancing again. Pick a piece of music that is a bit challenging for both of you. Gabriel, when you begin to feel like you have to open the door, stop dancing, as if a spell were cast, suspending you in time, and I will then pause the music.'

Maria goes over to her iPad, searches for a song, gives me the iPad, and walks back to Gabriel. Gabriel softly invites Maria into his embrace. This time I'm determined to watch and not get swept away. I touch 'play' on the iPad.

Nothing is presenting itself. Nothing sticks out. Not a thing, and then Gabriel stops. I walk over. 'Gabriel, what are you sensing?' 'I feel Maria's hand on my back and a tension down her left arm. I feel her pushing down on me to get closer to me, but it isn't working. This makes me feel closed in and locked out.'

I see Maria doing her best to correct herself. 'Maria, just go back to what you were doing. Are you back?' 'Yes, I am.' 'Good. Stay like that.'

'Gabriel, sense my hand under the back of your skull. Without any muscular effort, ever so slightly and easily, tilt your head back as if you were pouring water out of a pitcher into a glass and let your skull rest in my hands.' He does, and as he does, he stops over-straightening his neck. I can see he's got his cervical curve back. I softly bring his head back into balance, now over a more supple neck. I place my other hand on his chest. 'Gabriel, just think about settling back the tiniest bit into your own body.' He does. He's incredibly responsive. I walk behind Maria, gently lift Gabriel's hand from her back, remove any stiffness in his arm, hand, and fingers and then tenderly place his hand back where it was.

I scurry back to my chair and touch 'play'. I let them dance for about a minute, then pause the music. 'How was that, Gabriel?' 'It was mysterious,' Gabriel says, looking a little puzzled. 'When we started dancing Maria was no longer pressing on my back. In fact, I felt a strange support coming from her hand. Her left arm was at rest and yet felt very light.'

'Great. Okay, Maria. Now it's your turn. Come over and choose another piece of music, this time something that's easy for both of you, something you both like. Dance for a while. Take the time you need to come together, and then when you begin to feel like Gabriel is asking something from you, when you begin to feel this split, just stop as we did before. Okay?' 'Okay.'

In no time Maria finds a piece of music and gives me the iPad. I can see Gabriel has a softer look about him. When they look ready I tap the 'play' button. I recognize the music immediately. It's *Oblivion* by Piazzolla, my favourite piece of tango music.

A sudden and deep aching fills my chest, memories of a woman I loved too much begin streaming through me. I snap myself out of it and turn my attention to where it belongs. What I'm seeing looks to me like communion made visible. An image appears of twins embraced within their mother's womb. I'm no longer seeing two people, only one loving sphere moving through space. And then Maria stops. I press the 'pause' button.

'There it is,' Maria says. 'I'm back on the dance floor. I'm beginning to think,' she says. 'What do you feel in Gabriel, and Gabriel, don't change anything,' I say. 'He wants something from me,' Maria says. 'And how, physically, do you feel he is trying to get it from you,' I ask? 'It's not so much physical. It's as if I feel his will.'

As Maria explains I sense and see a little fear in her body. Her scapulae have retracted slightly and her lower back is overworking. 'Maria, rest your feet inside of your shoes. Place some attention not only under the heels of your shoe, but under the heels of your feet,' I say resting the tip of my index finger on her sacrum. 'Let your tongue rest inside your mouth. And let your scapulae rest as well.' Watching a huge breath enter her body, I get back to the chair and touch 'play'.

I'm watching, and listening, but mostly I'm feeling a world made of sadness and beauty passing before my eyes.

I can see that Maria is back outside in a vast space. I listen to Piazzolla's last note as it disappears down a long, dark corridor. I look up, and it's as if Maria and Gabriel had died in each other's arms.

I'm crying, crying for myself and somehow for everyone.

Somehow managing to get the words out of my mouth I say, 'Maria. Gabriel. Let's sit down. What did you find out? Was it interesting?'

'Very,' Gabriel begins. 'I feel a little bad. I mean, here I am thinking Maria is doing something that's getting in my way and all along it is me who is getting in my way,' he says, looking over to Maria, head bowed.

'And the same is true for me,' Maria says. 'When I feel separate from Gabriel it's because I am separating myself from Gabriel. And it's making me wonder about my relationship with my husband, and with my parents. Maybe I'm separating myself from them too.'

There's a long silence, and then Gabriel says, 'My teacher once told me, when I was going through a particularly hard time in my life, that every dancer brings their whole life onto the dance floor, and that anything and everything we cannot do in our lives we cannot do when we dance. That, he said, is what makes Tango so difficult, and what makes it so important. It's like that scene in *The Tango Lesson* when Pablo Veron sees Delacroix's image of Jacob wrestling with the angel. He's wrestling for his very life.' (Fig. 23.)

I feel myself wanting to agree, to add something. But I don't.

'I hate to stop. I wish we could go on forever. I feel like I should pay you for the privilege of watching you dance. I'm deeply moved.'

Fig. 23.

For the rest of the day, in my mind, I see Gabriel and Maria dancing to Piazzolla's *Oblivion*. I'm thinking about all that I can't do in my life.

Unable to sleep, I open my laptop and google 'Jacob wrestles with the angel'.

25. And Jacob was left alone; and there wrestled a man with him until the breaking of the day.

26. And when he saw that he prevailed not against him, he touched the hollow of his thigh; and the hollow of Jacob's thigh was strained, as he wrestled with him.

27. And he said: 'Let me go, for the day breaketh.' And he said: 'I will not let thee go, except thou bless me.'
28. And he said unto him: 'What is thy name?' And he said: 'Jacob.'
29. And he said: 'Thy name shall be called no more Jacob, but Israel; for thou hast striven with God and with men, and hast prevailed.'

Genesis 32:22-31

'That is what makes Tango so difficult, and what makes it so important,' I hear Gabriel's teacher whispering to me, as Piazzolla's last note disappears down that long, dark corridor and I fall into a deep, womb-like sleep.

4 SING FOR ME

In Temma, Osaka, eight of us sit together at a Spanish restaurant after a full day of study. 'Sometimes I really wonder about my voice. I don't know why it's so high,' Atsuko says. I notice when Atsuko speaks she looks like a little girl. There's a cute tilt of the head, sparkling eyes, a happy smile. 'Who knows,' I say. 'It could be structural. Then again it might not be. What does your voice sound like to you?' 'It sounds like everyone else's voice. Just normal,' she says.

'You know Atsuko, what your voice sounds like really doesn't matter so much. You're emotionally expressive, articulate, and easy to understand. It is like your voice is a piccolo, that's all. When you first hear a piccolo it sounds weird, too high, but then if someone is a good musician they can make beautiful music with that little instrument.

'I'm wondering why, to you, your voice sounds like everyone else's. If you hear your voice as the same as everyone else's voice, you'd have little impulse to change it.' 'But everyone else thinks my voice is too high,' Atsuko says.

'Atsuko, Alexander once said, "The things that don't exist are the most difficult to get rid of."' Atsuko looks puzzled. 'You see, your high voice doesn't exist for you. As far as your ears are concerned, you don't have a high voice.

'Atsuko, sing for me. Sing some little song you like.' The sparkling red wine having loosened everyone up, Atsuko begins singing *Sukiyaki, Ue O Muite Arukou.* 'Astuko, do you know a song that has a fuller range, some lower notes?' I ask. Mari, sitting next to her, begins singing a song I don't recognize. Astuko knows it and joins in. Without effort she drops down into the lower notes. 'Do you hear that, Atsuko?' She looks surprised and nods yes. 'Sing it again,' I ask. She does. 'There it is again! Did you feel that? That may be your real voice, what your voice sounds like when you're not holding it up.'

We were all relaxing, eating Japanese tasting tapas with chopsticks. The sparkling red wine the restaurant had given us for free, to lure us in, was now finished, and beer mugs had mysteriously appeared in front of everyone. I went no further, captivated as I was by Atsuko's changing voice.

'*Otsukaresama deshita*' (which means 'good job, we deserve to be tired'), I say, lifting up my beer glass. And whoever bought me this beer, *Doumo.* Thanks.'

Sometimes it's enough just to get something started.

SEEING PEOPLE

1 THE BINDING SPELL

There is so much to be seen when one reaches the point of being able to see . . .[17]

F. M. Alexander

Because I often do my work in groups, my trainees get to watch me work with lots of different people. They see I'm not working solely with a person's body. They see that, at heart, I am not a body worker. They see a person who works with people's beings through their bodies. They want me to teach them how to do that.

Teaching my trainees about their bodies and about how to move well is fairly straightforward. Teaching my trainees how to use their hands effectively is more challenging. Teaching my trainees how to see people in their entirety has been surprisingly difficult. But it is getting easier. I'm figuring something out.

When I was nine years old my friend asked me, 'Why do you stare at people?' I said, 'I don't stare at people; I look at them.' He didn't agree. There was no way to know I would become a person who made my living staring at people. I prefer to think of it as beholding people, holding people's beings in my eyes. That's a big part of my job. How does one behold a person? Here's what I do and, more importantly, what I don't do.

Just as some psychiatrists have devised terminology for different psychic forces – e.g. Freud's 'ego', 'id', and 'superego', or Eric Berne's 'parent', 'adult', and 'child', or Fritz Perl's 'top dog', 'underdog' – my observations tell me there are also physical forces worthy of their own names. Once you know the names for these physical forces – I refer to them as bodies – you can begin to see these different bodies at work within a person's physical body. Eckhart Tolle's 'pain body' is a good example. Once you can see these bodies within the body you begin to understand why people hold themselves the way they do, why they move the way they do, and sometimes why they think, feel, and behave the way they do.

Many somatic-oriented educators first see what I call 'the postural body'. When looking at the postural body we look for the relationships between parts of the body, one to the other: the relationship between the head and the neck, the ribs and the arm structure, the spine and the pelvis, etc. We look for hypertension and hypotension, we look for asymmetries, curvatures, twists, and torques. We look for how people are pulling themselves down, lifting themselves up, pressing themselves in, pushing themselves out, holding themselves back.

All well and good, but this is not where the act of beholding begins. Beholding is not observing; it's not entirely objective. Beholding is personal, felt, empathetic, intuitive, and profoundly subjective. And very much so, beholding is aesthetic.

I begin aesthetically. It may sound odd but initially I look at people as if they were living sculpture, frozen in time, under a binding spell. I behold their sculptural body. When we look at sculptures of humans we don't look at their posture. We see expression. We see the visible manifestation of thoughts and feelings. 'To express' literally means to 'press out.' Thoughts and feelings are pressed out from within, embedded, embossed into the physical body. We sculpt ourselves from the inside out.

Here are photos I took of human sculptures (Figs. 25–29). I love human sculptures because human sculptures let me stare at them for as long as I want. When you look at these photos, immediately

Fig. 25.

Fig. 26.

Fig. 27.

Fig. 28.

Fig. 29.

you will see the sculptural body: thoughts and feelings pressing out into the body, the body frozen in time, under a spell. Immediately you will know the difference between seeing the postural body and seeing the sculptural body. As you look at these photos with your eyes, allow yourself to kinaesthetically empathize with what you are seeing. Take the image into your body and being. Sense how the image makes you feel.

Seeing the sculptural body is easy. It comes naturally to us. Unconsciously, we do it all the time. It's only a matter of learning to do it consciously.

When I work with a student I usually work with them in front of other students. At first this makes most people a little nervous. Most people do not like people staring at them. They feel people are criticizing them, finding fault, judging them. They may feel people don't like them, or reject them. That's why, as a teacher, my first task is to create a space that feels profoundly safe. I do that by teaching everyone how to see sculpturally.

My job is to transport my students out of the world of right and wrong. As Rumi so beautifully said, 'Out beyond ideas of wrongdoing and right-doing there is a field; I'll meet you there.' But how do we bring our students into a field beyond right and wrong? To what field is Rumi referring?

The sculptural body lives within the realm of art. There is no right and wrong art. It's a thoroughly subjective world. I get my students to see that all people, no matter what they look like, are aesthetically beautiful. There is always composition, proportion, perspective, contrast, balance, colour, light, shadow, line, texture, structure, ground, space, shape, depth happening right before our eyes.

'Aesthetic' means to appreciate. It also means to feel. That means aesthetics is really another word for beholding. Once my students have entered this world of beauty, this field, the feeling in the entire room shifts. You can almost hear it . . . safety all around. Carl Rogers, originator of client-centred therapy, knew what it meant to behold someone. Rogers lived in the field beyond right and wrong.

One of the most satisfying experiences I know is just fully to appreciate an individual in the same way I appreciate a sunset. When I look at a sunset . . . I don't find myself saying, 'Soften the orange a little on the right hand corner, and put a bit more purple in the cloud colour' . . . I don't try to control a sunset. I watch it with awe as it unfolds. It is this receptive, open attitude which is necessary to truly perceive something as it is.[18]

Look for sculptural bodies on subways, at airports, in cafés. They are everywhere. If you are a somatic educator, the sculptural body is a good place to begin. The postural body lies within the sculptural body, but now it can be seen in context, as a physical manifestation of a person's being, of their psyche, their soul, their life.

As a person changes under my hands, the sculptural body changes, and the students see it. They feel it. Often they are emotionally moved because no longer are they merely seeing a person's body. They are seeing a person, a person they suddenly feel they know, because now that they are beginning to see them they are beginning to know them. As the person changes, they see the person emerging, as if through a fog. A binding spell, cast long ago, begins to lift, to fade. And there a person stands, visible, freed, unveiled.

2 IN THAT DEEP PLACE

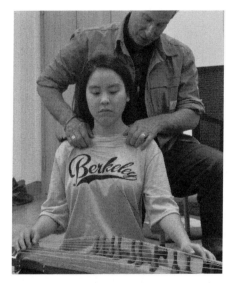

Fig. 30.

Let's imagine I'm teaching my trainees, and you are in the class with us.

'Okay. Why am I behind my student, my person?'

You want the group to be able to see.

It makes you kind of invisible. Maybe that makes it easier for her to attend to herself and her instrument.

Maybe you are supporting her back slightly with your lower leg.

'All are true. What seems to be working inside of my own coordination and what could be better? I am the first to tell my students that my use, my level of organization within myself is often not great, that I am my slowest student.'

Your right arm looks a little retracted, pulled up.

'Yes, thank you. It's good for me to know that. That helps me. Where are my hands, how am I using them, and what are they doing?'

They're under her clavicles, right at that place where the clavicles begin to curve up. It looks like you're catching, kind of scooping up the left side of her body more successfully than the right side. And the fingers on your left side look like they are functioning more independently, each finger saying something distinct, whereas the left fingers look less differentiated. The left hand looks like it's wearing a glove, and the right hand looks like it's wearing a mitten.

But take a look at her shoulders. Her right arm is slightly back and so is Bruce's. And her instrument is further back on that side and her hand too. Her left shoulder is slightly forward. Her left arm is more extended. It looks like both their torsos are rotating a tiny bit to the right to get parallel with the instrument.

Her left hand looks easier than her right hand.

Your thumbs are soft and light.

'Good. So you're seeing how I've chosen to orient myself around my person, where my hands are, and how I'm using them. That's a start. How would you describe the direction I am inviting the person to go?'

It looks like you're directing her attention in toward her upper ribs and up under her clavicles.

And, at the same time, up and out.

'What's happening as she goes with me?'

Her head is finding its balance on the spine, and it's almost like her eyes are settling back into her skull, and she looks like she's looking down on her instrument from up on high.

She's lengthening up the front without shortening down the back.

She looks focused and calm and strong, like a Buddha.

She looks like she goes to Berkeley and is proud of that.

'So from looking at me, what would you guess I'm thinking about, or sensing, to bring about that change?'

You're thinking about your own coordination?

'Good guess, but no, I am not, at least not exclusively. I don't think too much about myself when I'm working. When I'm working I feel more like a musician who is in a live jam. I've done my homework. I've practised a lot. I'm not thinking about technique. I am playing music.'

You're thinking about her.

'That's closer. But when I am at my best there is no "I", and there is no "she". There is only "us". I'm not thinking about me, and I'm not thinking about her. We're inside of one event, one experience. We are in an "overlap". Our circles are intersecting, and expanding, each into the other, and away from one another. We're together, inside of that shared space. We're in meeting. We're changing together. We're changing each other.'

'How do you think I am feeling?'

There's a kindness I'm picking up.

Pleasure.

'Yes and yes. You see, I'm "in-forming" her, but at the same time I'm nurturing her. I'm feeding her and breathing her, through touch. I'm helping to make her strong and proud and capable. That's why I like to think about her as my person. Sure, she's my student, and she's learning from me. But humans need more than knowledge to grow. Humans need to be nurtured.'

'On a deeper level, she's not my student, and I am not her teacher. In that deep place, together, we are growing into ourselves, and at the same time, we are coming out of ourselves.

'Can you see that?'

3 TEARS OF RECOGNITION

A woman wanted me to watch her teaching yoga. That's part of what I do; watch people work. I coach them as to how to do what they do more easily, more pleasurably, more meaningfully, more effectively.

Kumi begins by simultaneously demonstrating and explaining how to do a particular yoga movement. Both her movements and explanations are clear. I watch the students watching and listening to Kumi. By the end they look slightly overwhelmed. 'How am I going to remember all of that?' I can hear them thinking.

I ask Kumi to stop. I tell her what, in my view, she did well. 'Kumi-san, your timing is good. You move beautifully. Your voice is clear and easy to hear,' I say. 'I'm wondering what would happen if you told your students you were first going to show them a yoga movement and that you wanted them only to watch. And then, as if you were alone, practising by yourself, what if you did that yoga movement in front of them, in silence. What do you think?'

Kumi agrees to give it a go. She tells her students what she is going to do, what she wants them to do. She sits in silence. It's the kind of silence you can hear. The students lean slightly forward, eyes wide open. Kumi begins. I can see she's in unknown territory. She doesn't do this when she teaches. She really wants to say something. I see her preparatory inhale, and before Kumi has the chance to speak I kindly whisper, 'Shhh . . .' She continues silently. By the end I can see pleasure and beauty in her face. So can the students.

'Okay, Kumi. Good job. What do you think about doing only the very first movement in that lovely sequence and then inviting the students to practise that movement on their own, at their own timing? Just for fun.' Kumi consents.

The students look excited. They begin. Again Kumi is getting ready to say something. I softly intervene. 'Kumi, come sit down over here next to me. Get some distance from your students. Just watch them. Look how different they are.' She's watching. Her eyes begin to water. 'Kumi, who are they? Who are they? Find out.' Her eyes lower. Her hand comes up over her eyes. She's crying. Strongly. Tears of recognition. 'I never really look at my students!' 'That's okay, Kumi. You do now.'

Frank Ottiwell, an Alexander teacher from whom I learned a lot, once said to me, 'Bruce, don't try to help your students. Get to know them instead.' Right then, Frank changed my way of teaching forever.

See them and they will begin to see. Listen to them and they will begin to hear. Know them and they will begin to understand.

4 IN THE BLINK OF AN EYE

He said he wanted to work on talking. 'In what situation are you seeing yourself talking?' I ask. 'I'm talking to people,' he says. 'Where are you?' I ask. 'I'm around a table with a group of people. We're out to dinner. It's loud, lots of people are drinking, conversing, loud music is playing in the background,' he says. As he describes the situation I see his thin legs crossed, his thin body curled over in a c-shape, almost in a circle. In between sentences, I see his eyes flutter up, a couple rapid, tense blinks, and then he speaks, his mouth hardly opening, his voice circling inside his mouth, a thin voice, everything thin, withered; a young man, old before his time.

'Here we go,' I say to the group. 'Let's get that table and put it close to this noisy heater. Play some rock and roll from that iPad. Get that large bottle of cold tea, and those cups, and let's sit around together.' In Japan, when you give an instruction like that, everyone gets up simultaneously, there's a swirl of commotion, the dust settles, and it's done. I place the thin man across from a good-looking woman who is an actress. I know she will draw him out, and maybe make him a bit nervous.

'Alright. We've been at this table for a while. We've had a couple of beers. We're loosening up. Let's see what happens. *Douzo*. Begin.'

The party begins. I disappear into the thin man's blind spot and watch. He is doing almost exactly what he did when he explained the situation to me, but more pronounced. Everyone is engrossed. You can almost see the food on the table.

'Okay, that's good,' I say. I squeeze into the group next to the thin man. I have him sit back. With my hands, I help him uncurl his spine, relax his stomach. I get him to lean back and receive support from the chair. I'm not sure what I want to do next, so I sit quietly for a good 15 seconds, without saying a word . . .

'Okay,' I say, addressing the group. 'Your eyes are open, right? Now, close your eyes. Good. Now open your eyes. Good. Let me ask you. Do your eyes really close and open?' I ask. The group is wondering where I am going with this. 'I mean, really, can an eyeball open and close? Do eyeballs do that? What opens and closes? What raises and lowers, folds and unfolds?' I ask. I am intentionally not looking at the thin man. I don't want him to worry about me watching him.

'When you are really sleepy,' I say to the group, 'when you can hardly keep your eyelids from closing, how do your eyelids feel? Go there. Imagine that. Sense that. Can you sense the weight, the thickness, of your eyelids? What's happening?' I ask, as I see everyone's blinking slowing way down.

Out of the corner of my eye I see the thin man. The tension in his face is gone, and his face no longer looks thin. His upper body looks wide. I'm noticing for the first time how broad his shoulders are. There's no anxiety left in the man. The thin man has become the calm man. No more flutter in the eyes. None.

'Imagine you're an alligator,' I say to the group. 'You're slowly sliding through the swamp, your large, weighty eyelids covering and closing over your round eyeballs . . . then sluggishly opening, only as far as they open on their own. Imagine yourself semi-submerged, the lower half of your eyes under the water.'

Nothing could disturb the calm man now. Nothing could make this man nervous.

'Okay. Time for lunch. I hear there's a great Indian restaurant on this block. I can't wait. *Doumo arigatou gosaimashita.* Good job,' I say.

At lunch the calm man sits at the head of the table, open, unafraid, his voice full and resonant. Alexander's work, when it works, can work miracles; quiet, little miracles that can change a person's life forever.

5 RETURNING TO WHO YOU ARE

———•═•═•———

The wind at her back, she sails into the room, stands right in front of me, a tad closer than most Japanese people do, and tells me how happy she is to see me again. Speaking very quickly, assuming I understand her perfectly, which I don't, she tells me (I am guessing), how it has been six years since she last took my workshop, that she has had many lessons with Yoshie-sensei, and that she is thrilled about having an individual lesson with me.

Feeling thrust upon, I manage to say, '*Yokatta*, I'm glad.' I invite her to sit down, choosing to sit a little further away from her than I do with most people.

Sensing this chasm, she scoots up to the very edge of her chair, overly upright, intensely cheerful.

'Chie-san, I'm so sorry I don't speak or understand Japanese. I'm still working on my English. That's why Masako is here with us. How have your lessons been going with Yoshie? What have you learned? How have you changed?,' I ask.

Chie tilts her head, looking a little confused, and replies, 'I never really think about it. I just go in for my lessons and feel better when I leave. Yoshie-sensei's a wonderful teacher. I love her hands and she's so nice.'

'Chie-san, remind me what you do again,' I ask.

'I teach kindergarten. It's a lot of fun. The children are wonderful. They're so cute. Of course it takes a lot of energy to keep up with them, and sometimes at the end of the day my back hurts, but

I'm fine because I have such a good Alexander teacher. You did a great job training her,' Chie says, smiling.

'Yoshie-sensei was a very self-motivated student,' I say. 'She took a deep interest in the philosophy behind Alexander's work. Yoshie-sensei was especially good at looking at herself honestly. She was interested in how her body functioned, but she was more interested in how she functioned as a person in the world.'

For the first time since entering the room I see Chie not smiling.

'Let's stand up. I'd like to see you walk, the way you'd walk down the street in Osaka,' I say.

Chie springs out of her chair and begins walking across the room. Rather than her 'glide to greet' walk, she has now assumed a 'spring in your step' walk. In my imagination I see champagne bubbles rising up through the flute of a Waterford crystal champagne glass.

'Great. What a lively walk. You have so much energy,' I say. I watch as her bubbles rise even higher.

'Chie, just keep your body exactly the way it is now. Don't move a muscle. Pretend you are a statue, in the park. Get as comfortable as you can inside your statue because you are going to stay here like this for a couple of minutes. We need a little time to see what you are doing.'

'What I see, Chie, and a lot of people do this, is that you take the energy that belongs in the back third of your body' (I say, as with the knife edge of my hand I slice down the side of her body, beginning at her skull behind her mastoid process, straight down to her heel), 'and you push the back third of your body forward into the centre third of your body,' I say, as I lightly push Chie's lower back up toward her chest. 'That pushes the centre third of your body into the front third of your body, and so the front third of your body pushes out in front of you.'

'At the same time, because of wanting to be up and spunky, you tighten your thighs and push down against the ground, while at the same time raising your chest, and face up a little.' The image of an unflagging female figurehead on the bow of a Viking ship floats through my mind.

'Don't move,' I say, as I see her wanting to correct herself. 'You are doing great. This is where you live for many hours of every day, and it may be one reason why your back hurts when you finish working.'

'Not quite yet, but in a moment I am going to help you return to who you are without this pattern.' I place one hand lightly on the back of Chie's neck just under her skull, and I calmly rest my other hand on her raised sternum, and simply wait . . . until she begins to cease raising her sternum up.

'I'm coming way down,' Chie says.

'Well, yes and no. Sometimes down is up. Just go with it and let's see what happens,' I say.

Again, I see Chie's face no longer smiling. I notice her breathing slowing down and deepening.

'How are you feeling, not in your body, but as a person?' I ask.

'I feel unfriendly. Actually, I feel mean,' Chie says.

'Right now that's a good thing. Just go with it, just for now.'

'Right now you are working more than you have to in your legs to stand up. Standing up is just not falling down. Can you imagine your skeleton balancing on its own, standing up by itself?' I ask.

With that idea Chie's whole body completely stops pushing up or pushing forward. Rather than champagne bubbles, I'm sensing under my hands a full, deep, dark Argentinian Malbec.

'I feel totally slumped over, like an old woman,' Chie says.

'Chie-san, that is what you feel you look like, what you imagine you look like. But what are you actually sensing? Let me ask you a couple of questions. Is your back comfortable?'

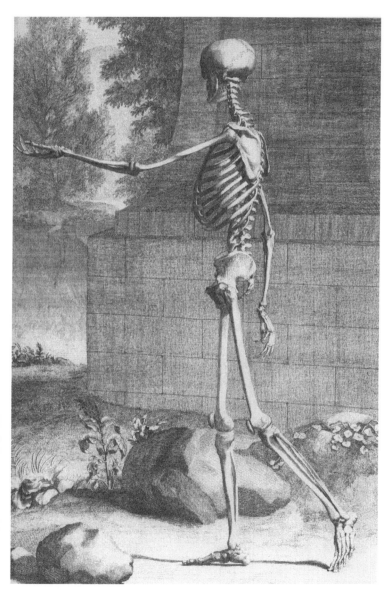

Fig. 31.

'Yes, very.'

'Is your whole body *physically* comfortable?'

'Yes, very.'

'How is your breathing?'

'Easy and slow, and calm.'

'No matter how strange it feels, just be like this, easily and loosely, and walk.'

I watch Chie as she walks around the room. 'How is that?' I ask.

'I don't feel like an old woman anymore. I can feel the ground under my feet. That feels good. I feel small and big at the same time. I don't feel like me. I don't know who this is,' Chie says.

'Do you feel mean and unfriendly?'

'Not any more. I feel . . . neutral, thoughtful.'

'Good work, Chie-san. Let's sit down.' This time Chie sits back against the back of the chair. I find myself wanting to sit closer to her, so I do.

'Now, let's stop and think together about what just happened. Let's see what you can learn about yourself,' I say.

I shuffle through my laminated prints of Albinus's engravings. I show Chie how Albinus shines light onto the figure from a particular angle, illuminating what he wants us to see. (Fig. 31.)

'Chie, can you see how the back half of the figure's head is lit, while the front is cast in shadow? And see the shadow on the underside of the skull?'

'Ah, it is as if he, Albinus, wants me to see that half of my skull is behind my spine. It is so clear,' she says.

I walk behind Chie and ask her to scoot her pelvis all the way into the back of the chair. 'Chie, rest the back of your skull into my hands as if your hairdresser was going to shampoo your hair,' I say. 'I promise to support the full weight of your head.' As Chie gives me the full weight of her skull, I slowly guide it back, up, and over her spine. 'Now the back of your skull is in the back third of your body,' I tell Chie.

I can see a little space between the wooden chair seat and the high vertical back of the chair. I pass my hand through that space and rest it on the top of her sacrum. My translator, Masako, holds the Albinus drawing out in front of Chie. 'The sacrum is in the back third of your body. Most of what you are seeing in the engraving is the tail end of the sacrum and coccyx, which is more vertical than the body of the sacrum, which is much more horizontal.' Putting the knife edge of my hand on a diagonal across the sacro-ilia joint, I give Chie the sense of the angle of the sacrum as it wedges itself in between the ilia. 'Can you imagine that? Can you see it and sense it at the same time?' I ask.

'*Hai*,' Chie says.

I place my hands on her scapulae as Chie looks at Albinus. 'Your scapulae are also in the back third of your body. Can you see that and sense that at the same time? And they are large, about the size of your hand when it's wide open. And they are shaped like the continent of Africa. Can you sense that?' I ask.

'*Hai.*'

'You're having an experience of your back, of the size and power and location of your back. In Noh drama there is a saying, "The eyes see forward but the spirit adheres to the back." Right now you are adhering to your back and when you are adhering to your back you can't push forward in the way you do. It's impossible.'

'Let's stand up, Chie.' I watch out of the corner of my eye. Instead of springing out of the chair, I watch her body smoothly fold and unfold out of the chair. I don't say anything about it. Chie stands, and I can see she's pushed again into the front third of her body.

'Chie. You are doing very well. Don't move. Just be where you are. You are doing it less, but can you sense that little push into the front third of your body? Can you sense how the back third is pushing forward a little and how your spirit is adhering less to your back?' I ask.

'*Hai.*'

'*Sugoi.* Great.'

'Now see what happens if you simply stop pushing.'

'Wow. I didn't do anything and it all fell back into place, all by itself.'

'That's what Alexander called non-doing. You didn't do anything to change. You simply stopped doing what you were doing and the rest happened by itself. I call that returning to who you are. My teacher, Marj Barstow, called it "a little bit of nothing".'

'Now that we are standing, let's see and sense how our heels are part of the back third of our body as well,' I say.

Masako holds the Albinus drawing in front of Chie. I point out how the heels are behind the ankle in the drawing, and how the ankles are in front of the heel. Then I point out how the heels are lower than the ankles, and the ankles are higher than the heels. 'And Chie, look at the two rocks, the smaller one in the foreground and the bigger one in the background. Clearly Albinus wants to direct our attention to the heels, don't you agree?' I ask.

'*Eeeehhhh,*' Chie exclaims!

I kneel down behind her onto one knee, placing my right hand down on her heel. Looking up at her head, I reach up and place my left hand all the way up under her skull. 'That's the back third of your body from top to bottom,' I say, feeling like I am in a yoga pose.

'*Sugoi.* When I'm like that it feels impossible for me to push into the front third of my body,' Chie says. 'That's the spirit adhering to the back, what Alexander called "back back". Eventually your back will become more important for you than your front,' I say, coming out of my yoga pose.

'We're running over our time a little. Is that okay with you?'

'*Hai.*'

'There is one more thing I'd like us to think about together. Let's sit down.'

'Alexander spoke of habits. It's a perfectly good word but I find myself using the word "patterns". We all acquire certain patterns, movement patterns, vocal patterns, and what I sometimes call persona patterns. Today we stumbled upon a persona pattern. A persona is the image of ourselves we present to the public. Often it's not really who we are. Behind the persona is the person who we really are. Sometimes we are afraid to let people see who we are behind the persona. We think it is somehow too plain, or not enough. But actually who we really are, without our persona, is what people are drawn toward, what they find beautiful and lovable.'

'You have a cheerful, energetic, bubbly persona. It is as if you are compelled to be happy and positive all the time. There's nothing wrong with being cheerful, positive and bubbly. It only becomes a problem when we feel we have to be that way for people all the time.'

'It's a little like an outfit. Clothes can express something about us, but they are not us. Our real body, the real us, is underneath our clothes. Our shoes are not our feet, right?'

'So today, Chie-san, you experienced who you are without your persona. That person is unfamiliar to you. That person is not unfriendly or mean. That person is calm and thoughtful. That person has many qualities you have yet to discover. Alexander's work is about living an examined life, about getting to know yourself, about getting in deep contact with who you really are.'

'Chie, now you have a way to find out. You know how to recognize your persona and you know how to sense it as a doing, and you know how to undo it. And once you undo it, you are free to find out who you are without it.'

'Thank you, Chie-san. Sorry for taking so much of your time.'

Chie bows and quietly leaves the room.

6 ALL IN A DAY'S WORK

———

There's the man who, when he talks, nervously looks up and to the right, blinking rapidly. I have no idea why. I don't bother to try and find out. I ask him to tell me what's difficult about his job. He begins to speak. I tap his arm the instant he begins to look up, which he is doing about every three seconds. He can't believe he looks up so much. Soon he's sensing it every time. 'As soon as you notice your eyes go up and to the right, stop everything, don't move, don't speak. Just ask yourself, "What would happen if I simply ceased looking up?"' He begins speaking. His eyes snap up and to the right. He stops. I can almost hear him asking the question. Immediately, on their own, his eyelids lower, his eyes begin to water, settling back into his eye sockets, while his entire body relaxes and he begins to breathe like a man just resuscitated. I continue asking him questions, and for the next minute he looks at me and speaks without once looking up.

There's the woman whose eyes are too big, too open. Since she was a little girl she was told her eyes were beautiful. I ask her if she can remember a time before anyone told her that her eyes were big and beautiful. She thinks for a long time and then says, 'No, I can't.' It is as if she was only born the moment people began to tell her how she looked.

There's a mom stooped over her year-and-a-half-old son in an effort to help him balance as he walks. The mom is unaware that, when she stands fully upright, her hand rests beside her son's head, and that her son's arm is fully capable of lengthening freely and easily well above his head. All her little son needs and really wants is to lightly hold her index finger. She takes my suggestion, stands up, offers her index finger, her son looks at it, takes it, and smiles.

There's the man who's uncomfortable stretching. He appears to be simultaneously stretching and keeping himself from stretching. I have him sense the difference between moving without producing a stretch, and moving while producing a stretch. I ask him to slowly and easily begin a movement and to continue the movement for as long as he can without producing a stretch. It doesn't matter how small the movement is. I have him do this several times. I suggest he begin to make movements in other directions, to make other curving or spiraling movements through his whole body without creating a stretch. I silently walk behind him, placing my hands almost imperceptibly on his arms, just above his elbows, following his movements, all the while educing an effortless release through his whole body. His movements become beautiful, free instead of constricted. His range has noticeably increased. 'How do you feel?,' I ask. 'I feel loose and awake,' he says. 'Isn't that what we're after when we stretch?' 'Yes,' he says, slightly bewildered.

There's the singer singing, gasping for air at the end of each phrase, her chest dropping out from under her, her shoulders curling forward, her chin lifting up, the back of her skull pushing into the back of her neck. You can hear her sucking in the air. She begins to sense what she's doing, begins to hear how she gasps. It's a beginning.

There's the business executive who says, '*eh*' (our 'um'), in between every sentence, who, when he leaves '*eh*' out, becomes crystal clear to understand, is filled with real confidence, thinks more clearly, and immediately wakes up everyone in the room.

There's an elderly man who likes to hike, but who has trouble putting on his backpack. He simply has not noticed that he could loosen one of his straps and then initiate a slight swing that allows the pack to almost slide onto his back by itself.

A woman is possessed by childish cute-isms she cannot stop. She's thirty-something but moves as if she is a nervous twelve-year-old. Knowing I often use my hands when I teach, she's warns me she's acutely ticklish. I nod. I ask her to walk over to me. Immediately what I refer to as a 'cute-ism' begins: quick, cute expressions like tilting her head and smiling with one hand covering her mouth, turning her right foot in, innocently blinking her eyes. She walks over. I ask her to walk back to where she was. After first producing a few unconscious cute-isms, she does. Without my being nice, but not mean, I tell her precisely what she is doing. The truth. I tell her the truth. I tell her to decide, gently but undeniably, to leave her cute-isms out entirely and just walk over. The smile comes off her face. She stands there for about ten seconds . . . then walks over. For five minutes, I have her leaving out her cute-isms and walking to different parts of the room. Throughout the entire weekend she looked and conducted herself like a mature woman. By the end of the workshop she seemed to forget she was ticklish. She accepted my touch, just like everyone else. I said nothing about it. Nor did I say anything about the disappearance of her cute-isms. There was no need. She had done her work.

There's the tai chi teacher whose tai chi form is already exquisite, and who gets even better when I suggest to her not to look down, that she first look in the direction where she is going, and then go there.

There's the nurse who feels she has to lean over her patient, bringing her head and eyes close to her patient to show she cares when, in fact, it makes her patient uncomfortable. The nurse discovers that when she simply stands where she is and looks at her patient while allowing her eyes to be above her upright spine, and speaks to her patient from there, this instills real trust and a sense of safety, exactly what she wants to do.

There's the toddler falling asleep on his mother's lap. The child is leaning back upon the mother's chest, his head fallen back, mouth open. The mother has her hands around the child's belly. The mother's shoulders are curled forward. There's some tension in her hands. Her knees are pressing one against the other, firmly closed, her feet turned in, her heels held up off the ground.

Not to wake the child, I quietly pull a chair up and sit down directly behind the mother. I sit in tandem with her. Softly placing my hands, one on either side of her neck, her neck tension releases, her head floats up atop her spine and, in rapid succession, her shoulders widen, her hands relax and appear larger, her thighs un-brace and rest on the chair, knees part a little, heels drop to the floor as her feet turn out ever so slightly.

At the same time the baby's mouth closes and he too regains his head poise. I look around the room. Several people are crying. I'm not sure why. I lean around the mother so I can see how she's doing. A ray of late afternoon light has entered through a window and is falling onto the mother's face. She looks like a Madonna and Child.

My work is done for the day. I will go out like so many working people do in Tokyo, with some friends, eat dinner and have a cold beer. I won't be watching how people move or speak. I won't be thinking about how they could do this or that more easily. I'll be sitting back, fading into the woodwork, happy not to be the centre of attention. There's nothing for me to do now but love people, exactly the way they are.

NURTURING PEOPLE

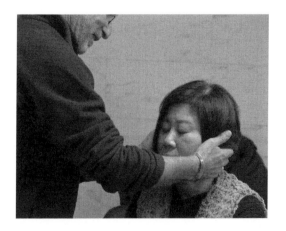

1 ONE SMALL GESTURE

OF KINDNESS

A mother, 70, has a son with cerebral palsy. He is now 45 years old. The mother is small and the son is not. For years the mother has lifted her son from his wheelchair to the toilet, and back again. I ask her to show me how she lifts her son up. The mother moves well. She has to.

'Chiyo-san, you do that very well. I'm sorry, but I'd like to see you do it one more time.'

'*Hai*,' Chiyo-san says, bowing quickly and sharply.

I notice an almost invisible gesture she makes as she gets ready to pick up her son. She quickly strokes the right side of her head, moving her thick, gray-streaked hair back behind her ear. I ask her to pause for a moment. I ask her if she felt the movement she just made. Chiyo says, 'No, I didn't do anything yet.' I said, 'Yes, you did.' I tell Chiyo what she did. I ask her to do it again, very slowly, consciously. She does. I ask her to do it again, and then again. I ask her to continue, but to do it now as if her mother were brushing her hair. She continues. Soon Chiyo begins to cry.

I say, 'Okay, Chiyo-san, go and lift up your son.' She doesn't move, doesn't speak. I wait. Then Chiyo says, 'I am too old to do this by myself. I need help.' She turns to her younger son who is in the room and asks him if he wouldn't mind helping her. He is happy to do it for his mom, and for his brother. Chiyo-san stands there watching her two boys.

2 TWO WORLDS

———◆◆◆———

There is another world, but it is in this one.[19]

Paul Éluard

O mata se. Thank you for waiting for me. I'm really sorry I am so late.
You say this, straight away, if you arrive late in Japan. Actually,
you say it even if you arrive on time because, by Japanese stand-
ards, if you arrive on time you are still late. You are only not late in
Japan if you are 15 minutes early. Then you can just say hello.

Given this cultural mandate one begins to understand what is
going on when seeing a trash collector running to get a trash can,
running back to the truck with the trash can, dumping the trash
into the truck, running back to return the trash can, running back
to the truck and, as the truck is in motion, jumping onto the trash
truck only to get to the next house, where the trash collector jumps
off the trash truck and begins running once again, this continuing
for roughly ten hours.

No wonder my friend Dr. Tanaka, who owns and runs a large
orthopedic clinic, a gifted and loved doctor, rushes continually.
He cannot seem to keep up with the number of people, every day,
who want to see him, people in pain: backs, knees, hips, shoulders,
necks; all hurting and in need of attention.

Dr. Tanaka sees me once a year. Knowing he has one session
a year, he gives me his undivided attention. Knowing I have only
one chance to work with him each year, I give him mine.

Dr. Tanaka asks me to look at him and to tell him what I see. Though I refrain from doing this with many of my students, with Dr. Tanaka I know it will be fine. He won't fall into the trap most students do when given such information. He won't freak out, thinking he's doing terrible things to his body. He won't immediately try to correct his dire condition. He'll just take in the information and begin wondering about it. As will I.

I take my first good look at Dr. Tanaka. A little taller than me, a little younger (both not difficult), he looks healthy: bright eyes, good skin colour, excellent muscle tone, not overweight, a nice sense of symmetry about him.

'You're looking good, Tanaka-sensei. Let's see what I see from the side.' My eye goes directly to the back of his neck. I reach up and say, 'This muscle interests me,' gently pinching it between my thumb and fingers so he can feel it. 'Maybe it's your trapezius but whatever muscle it is, it's working hard. There must be a reason.' I see there's no natural curve in his cervical spine. He looks like he's just started to bow and then suddenly stopped before his body had a chance to follow, leaving his neck over-extended and stiff. For a second I see the neck of one of those creepy gargoyle drain spouts you see as you walk around Notre Dame. 'Dr. Tanaka, you carry your head a bit in front of your body in a way that over-straightens your neck, so chances are that muscle, and others, have to work to counterbalance the displaced weight of your head.'

'And your body also inclines slightly forward from your ankles, a little like a ski jumper in flight.' I bend down and feel his calves which, as I suspected, are working hard, keeping him from falling over. His 'glutes' are squeezing together and hiking up. I move and sit down in front of Dr. Tanaka, as if I were one of his patients, and suddenly I see what he's doing. There before me is a man who looks like he's been racing to get to where he has to be and, once there, jams on the brakes and stops, frozen in the slightest gesture of a bow as if to say, 'O *mata se*! Thank you for waiting for me. I'm really sorry I am so late.'

'Tanaka-sensei. Let's sit down,' I say, pointing to a chair. He sits down. 'I'm your patient. Take my pulse.' Being learned in Chinese medicine as well, I know pulse taking is an important ritual for Dr. Tanaka. It's his first physical contact with his patient. True to form, Dr. Tanaka jumps into action. When I sense he's totally into it, I ask him to just stay where he is, not to move, and sure enough, he has clicked into his particular way of being engaged, of serving his patient.

'Dr. Tanaka, I'm wondering if you have to look at your fingers? You can't see the pulse, right?' 'Right,' he says. 'So keep taking my pulse, slowly look up a little toward the ceiling, letting your neck go into a comfortable arch, then close your eyes, and just continue reading my pulse. Now, leave your eyes closed, softly rotate your head slightly forward, letting it rest on top of your spine. Roll back ever so slightly on your sit bones and relax your butt muscles, because you don't need them now. Sense your body breathing itself and just continue taking my pulse. And you might as well relax your left elbow, so you don't have to work so hard in your left shoulder.'

For the first time since we began Tanaka-sensei looks calm, quiet, and comfortable, not like a busy doctor but still like a doctor for sure. That large neck muscle is no longer protruding. He's got the natural curve back in his cervical spine. He's not rushing. He's not ahead of himself. He's within himself, and he's with me, more than ever. Like the good student Dr. Tanaka is, I can see him drinking in the experience, quietly coming to an understanding about how he does what he does. What he's most happy about, he tells me, is not how good he feels but how clearly he can feel my three pulses under his fingers. I think to myself, 'There it is, the difference between Japan and America,' feeling grateful to have had the benefit of living in Japan with so many other-centred people.

Seeing Dr. Tanaka looking so relaxed and attentive reminds me of something I read years ago in the tai chi classics, words of wisdom gleaned over 600 years about the workings of the mind and the body. Dr. Tanaka practises tai chi. My guess is he'll resonate with what I am about to say.

'In the tai chi classics, Tanaka-sensei, they tell us to have the mind of a sober man and the body of a drunk. I call it Matcha Mind and Sake Body. Sit back in your chair and relax into your Sake Body.' That appears to be easy for him, but I see his head drifting off to the left as if he's falling asleep. 'Tanaka-sensei, open your eyes and without losing your Sake Body rouse your Matcha Mind.'

'*Muzukashii!*' That's really hard, Dr. Tanaka says. 'I can't do it!'

'That's because you've got working hard and muscle tension paired up, and you've got releasing muscle tension and sleeping paired up. Meditation, as I understand it, is cultivating an inverse relationship between tension and attention. The more you increase your mental attention, the more you want to decrease your muscular tension.' Saying it this way, I can see Dr. Tanaka gets it.

'Okay, sensei. I know you want me to watch you playing your *shakuhachi*, so go get it.' (A *shakuhachi* is a traditional bamboo flute.) Tanaka-sensei springs out of his chair and starts running toward the door. '*Choto mata kudasai!* Please wait a minute, Dr. Tanaka! I want you to decide, deep inside your body, not to rush. Don't worry about me. I'm fine. See what it feels like if you don't rush. Just find out what happens.'

Dr. Tanaka calmly leaves the room. He's gone for about two minutes. When he returns he's got a different expression on his face. 'How was it?' I ask. 'It was really different. I began to see this building, this clinic. I began feeling how long I have worked here, and my father before me,' he said. His voice was sad, but there was love and gratitude shining from his eyes.

'Dr. Tanaka. We will get to playing the *shakuhachi*, I promise. But I'd like to talk to you for a minute. Not teaching. I just want to tell you something from my heart. Is that okay?' '*Hai*,' he says.

'Look, we are going to die . . . someday. You could rush and run toward your death, or you could walk toward it the way you just walked to get your *shakuhachi*. Two different worlds. Which one do you want to live in for the time you have left?'

And there it was, the moment, the shift, the shift in a person's soul.

We did get to the *shakuhachi*. The usual things happened. Resonant sound. Freer breathing. Better phrasing. More fun. But inside of the greater scheme of things it didn't seem all that important.

We thanked each other, many times, as you do in Japan before saying good-bye. '*Yoi otoushi wo*. Have a happy New Year, Dr. Tanaka.'

It's five o'clock and already evening as I walk alone down a small, empty street toward the train station. A soft, misty rain falls. Most Japanese open their umbrellas and rush along to wherever they're going. I don't mind getting wet. Why run? It's raining everywhere.

3 ON BECOMING A PERSON

There's an advantage in not understanding a word people say.

For four months a year I live in Coyote, New Mexico, a small Spanish community comprised, from what I can gather, of about five large families that have lived in the village for 400 years. Everyone speaks Spanish. They speak English for me out of the kindness of their hearts.

My school is based in Germany. I spend three months a year traveling and teaching in Europe. Mostly, I don't understand what anyone is saying. The rest of the year I live in Osaka, Japan, where again, I've no idea what anyone is talking about.

This is no mistake. I was meant to be linguistically impaired. I was meant to spend hours upon hours of my life simply watching people move, gesture, socialize, and work. I was meant to spend hours upon hours not talking, just watching and listening, listening not to people's words, but to their voices and, more importantly, to their silences. I live much of my life like a baby who cannot yet understand language, cannot speak, and cannot read. That's why I'm good at my job.

My students for the weekend are all Japanese psychologists. After several hours of preparation, they are now ready to show me what it's like for them when they work with their patients. Half of the therapists will be role-playing patients. The remaining therapists will simply do what they do. One therapist works in a jail with prisoners. Another goes to homes where depressed teenagers will not come out of their rooms. Another assists in a community centre for poor, mentally vulnerable people who cannot find a place in the world. Another helps victims devastated by domestic violence and sexual abuse.

'I'm not going to know a word you are saying,' I tell them. 'I don't want to know. I can be of more help to you if I don't. My job is to hear the unspoken.'

And so it begins . . .

The Boxer

Yoko is sitting across from a patient who's angry and taking it out on her. He's unusually big for a Japanese man. He's loud, truculent, or so it seems to me. He's sitting back, legs spread wide apart, belly protruding. His fists rest one on each of his big thighs. He's pouting. He looks hurt but his knitted brow and glaring eyes tell me he's also furious. I'm standing far away, as I often do, off to the side. At some point Yoko's torso collapses. She's leaning to the right. Her head has slid forward in front of her body, toward her patient. She's pinching her brow together. She looks concerned. After about 30 seconds Yoko shifts over to the left, straightens her spine, pushes slightly back with her back against the back of the chair, pulls the nape of her neck back, folds her arms against her chest and tucks her chin. She looks wary, skeptical.

This dropping down to the right and going forward toward the patient, then shifting and pulling up to the left and pulling away from the patient repeats itself several times. Suddenly I see it, a boxer dodging punches, ducking down to the right, pulling back to the left. Yoko's doing her best to avoid being hit.

When Yoko drops into her concerned pose I silently walk over to her and quickly but softly place one of my hands over her hands, and the other on top of her head as I quietly tell Yoko to stay just as she is for a minute. (If I don't place my hands over a person before

I ask a person to stop, invariably they immediately move and try to correct themselves.) Yoko's now frozen, sculpture-like, ducking down to the right. 'Yoko-san, this is where you spend a couple of hours every day. Now, where do you go when your body gets tired of being here?' I ask. Without any hesitation she pulls up and over to the left. 'And here is where you spend another couple of hours a day,' I say. Yoko slowly nods her head. She's getting it. 'Yoko, why do you think you do that?' I ask. '*Wakarimasen.* I've no idea,' she says, 'but I can feel I do this a lot. My body knows these places very well.'

'Would you like to know what it looks like to me?' I ask. '*Hai*,' she says. 'It looks like you're a boxer dodging punches.' I stand up, raise my fists in front of my face and show her how a boxer moves when dodging punches. I sit down and do the same thing, more slowly. Then I slow it down even more and mimic what she does when listening to this patient. Yoko covers her mouth with her hand, as many Japanese women do, and lets out a big laugh of recognition. She looks ashamed, amused, and relieved.

'Yoko-san, would you like to try something different?' I ask. '*Hai*,' she says. 'I'm going to have you sit smack in front of this patient,' I say. I get her hips squarely back in the chair, get the chair to give her some back support, and I bring her into her full stature. She looks about twice the size. 'Now see what happens if you decide to look easily but squarely into your patients' eyes, and no matter what your patient throws at you, I want you to remain in front of him, resting inside your big, soft, powerful self. Have you decided? Have you made a commitment to yourself?' I ask. I wait until I can see she has. Turning to this large, splayed-out man, I say to him, 'Okay, let her have it!'

Everyone is waiting for the patient to explode. Nothing. We continue to wait. Nothing. 'What's the matter?' I ask the patient. 'I can't yell at her. She's right in front of me and I can't yell at her. I just can't do it,' he says.

The Bead Maker

Kyoko is working at a community centre for poor, mentally troubled people. She walks over to a table where two patients are making necklaces. The patient on the right, appearing frustrated and slightly hysterical, asks Kyoko to help her string a tiny bead. Kyoko bends way over, rounding her back like a question mark, pulls the string and the bead very close to her eyes, looks over the tops of her glasses, her head just inches away from the patient's head, and begins stringing the bead. Kyoko's totally into what she's doing so she doesn't notice me next to her. Softly, I place one hand on the top of her hanging head, the other on her rounded upper back, and quietly ask her to just be there for a moment. 'This is what you do,' I say without judgement. 'Just sense it and take it in. How about we go about this another way? What do you think?' I get a nod. Consent.

'Pull up a chair. Sit down. Make yourself comfortable,' I say. She rounds over in the chair much the same way as she does when she is standing up. At the same moment, both patients start asking her for help. I can see her panicking and feeling like she's got to work quickly. 'Kyoko, you're doing well. Just be with me. Follow my hands,' I say. I give a delicate upright impulse around her neck, and her spine uncurls. With my hands, I invite her shoulders to open apart, and I ask her just to look at her patients from where she is now. 'I'm so far away,' she says. 'Well, yes and no,' I say. 'You are sitting at the table with them. You're on the same level with them. They're right here. Let's continue.' They both start to talk. Kyoko turns to the patient on her left and calmly listens, and looks at the problem she's having with her beads. 'I'm not rushing,' Kyoko says. 'When there's space, there's time. It just works that way,' I say. 'Let's continue.' The patient on the right is supposed to continually interrupt, but instead she's just sitting there waiting. 'I know I am supposed to give her a hard time, but I can't do it. I just don't want to,' the patient says.

THE PRISONER

Ridiculing Makoto, making snide remarks, the prisoner sits there feeling superior. Makoto looks hurt, weak, and helpless. It looks to me like they're both behind bars, both imprisoned, both locked in their own worlds.

My eyes immediately go to Makoto's legs. Her legs look like they belong to someone who cannot walk, who hasn't walked for years. Toes turned inward, knees fallen together, stomach compressed, pelvis rolled back, chest hollowed out, shoulders curled and drooping forward. Her body looks like it's sunken in a wheelchair, but there is no wheelchair. Above her caved-in body is a strikingly beautiful face. Makoto's mouth and full lips softly push forward in space while her forehead tilts back slightly. Her long neck is softly buckled forward like a swan. Her eyelids are half closed. There's something overwhelmingly kind and tender about her, this large, sensual, expressive face, and below a body lifeless, lacking support, without structure.

It takes about twenty minutes but I am in no rush. Slowly, from the bottom up, I build her structure, as if I'm building a wall. 'Makoto, this is your left foot. We want it to live on the left side of your body, away from the midline. This is your right foot. It lives on the right side of your body, on the other side of the world. This is east,' I say, pointing to the left, 'and this is west,' I say, pointing to the right. 'And so it is with your ankles and your lower legs and your knees,' I tell her. 'Your legs live on different sides of the planet with the Pacific Ocean between them.' Makoto's legs are now apart but not far apart, nothing that would draw attention from others.

But for her it feels enormous. I touch each part of her body as I name each part, as if I am introducing her to her body for the first time. I hear myself sounding a lot like Mr. Rogers on the children's television series 'Mr. Rogers' Neighborhood'. 'From under your feet up to your knees constitutes 25 percent of your height. These are your knees. They're the largest joints in your body. They're huge, like extra large grapefruits. These are your thighs, from your knees all the way back to your hip joints. Thighs are big and wide. The muscles within the thigh are the most powerful muscles in the body, constituting another 25 percent of your height. They too live in separate hemispheres with the Pacific Ocean between them. This is your pelvis. Your sitbones are lowest, like the ground floor, then the hip joints are the first floor, then the sacrum is the second floor, and then the iliac crests are the third floor. So your pelvis has great width, depth, and height. It's like a great bowl full of fruit.'

'This is your spine,' I say. Slowly, from the bottom I begin sliding my hands, one up the back and the other up the front, letting her feel each curve of her spine and the transitions between the curves. 'Think of the back of your skull as another curve of your spine.' As she senses that idea her whole spine suddenly springs up, like a vertical accordion. She has a look of awe on her face. She can't believe what is happening to her. 'Makoto, I know this has to feel totally different, but just go with it. You're doing great,' I say. Mr. Rogers continues. 'This is your arm structure: clavicle, scapula, shoulder joints, humerus, ulna, radius, wrists, palms, fingers. Makoto, your outstretched arm structure, from fingertip to fingertip, your wingspan, is as wide as you are tall. This is your body. This is the size of your body.' Even though I am taking so much time, the entire group is captivated because a transformation is happening right before their eyes. And not just before their eyes. Everyone seems to be kinaesthetically empathizing. Everyone is filling out and opening up.

With the tip of my index finger, ever so lightly, I touch Makoto's lips. 'Makoto, this is your mouth, your lips, and you have them protruding a little in front of your face.' I place my other index finger on the corner of her eye. 'And here are your eyes. Can you feel how they are falling back in relation to your mouth that's sliding forward?' I can see her exact moment of recognition, such a beautiful moment, the mind connecting to the body through the kinaesthetic sense. '*Hai*, I feel it,' she says. '*Sugoi*. Great. Now this is likely to feel very strange but give it a go. Follow my hands.' I guide Makoto's skull. It's rotating around like a ferris wheel. The mouth shifts back under the eyes as the eyes come up over the mouth. 'I feel like a king on a throne,' Makoto says. 'Not a bad thing,' I say. 'You don't look like that. You just look like a strong, kind person. Okay, Makoto, I want you to say something to this man, but I don't want the words to come out of your mouth, I want them to pour out of your eyes, like water pouring out a very full pitcher of water. Make a decision to leave your mouth, without effort, exactly where it is.' As soon as Makoto even thinks about saying something I can see her mouth begin to protrude forward. It takes several tries, each time asking her again to decide deeply. 'Let that decision spread through you as if it were streaming through every vein in your body.' I glance at the prisoner and notice that his body no longer looks rebellious. There's no smirk on his face. Makoto is silent for a while. I can see it. She's sticking with her decision against a fierce life pattern. Then she says something in Japanese. I don't know what. It doesn't matter. But what I do know is that she spoke from a place of compassionate authority. And I do know that, at that moment, the bars were gone, both the therapist's and the prisoners' bodies were unlocked. They were free.

And so it went for the remainder of the workshop. After the workshop some of us go out for dinner, one of my favourite things to do. Ayumi, the organizer of the workshop, tells me that in Japan psychotherapy is founded primarily on the work of Carl Rogers, on listening and empathy. I smile, remembering when I was 25 years old, reading *On Becoming A Person*, and feeling like Carl Rogers was my dad. On every page I could hear his voice speaking to me from some deep place of love and kindness. I remember wanting to be like him. Maybe, 40 years later, I have become like him, sitting there, giving each student the time it takes for them to know who they are and who they could become.

4 THE MASTER

———◆••••◆———

'When have you experienced yourself lost, without support, help-less and afraid?' I ask a group of fairly new Alexander teachers. 'Can you see where you are, the situation you are in; can you see what's going on?'

Michiko, a small, middle-aged woman in the back of the room says, 'I'm going through a divorce. I have another session in court next week where I have to plea for the custody of my children. I am terrified of losing them.'

All eyes in the room lower at once.

'Thank you. Let's see if there is a way, through Alexander's work, to help ourselves when we really need it, when we're feeling threatened, when our lives are hanging in the balance. How can we develop the wherewithal to be how we want to be in these situations? How can we not only survive them, but meet them?'

'Michiko. Look around and see who can help you set up your scenario. Look and see how you can best arrange the space.' Everyone springs into action. Seriously playful commotion fills the room. I sit back and watch as the space is transformed into a courtroom.

In the front of the room sits a judge. Michiko's husband and his lawyer sit to the judge's left, Michiko and her lawyer to the right. I've got a translator behind me, ready to whisper into my ear.

The judge begins. 'We are here today to determine who is most deserving of the privilege of caring for your children. As you know, I do not approve of divorce. I believe children should grow up with a mother and a father in the same house. But for whatever reasons, both of you seem incapable of doing this. Michiko, what do you have to say for yourself?'

'Judge, I am the parent who has spent the most time with my children. I am the one who cooks for them, who packs their lunches, who takes them and picks them up from school, who helps them with their homework. I am the one who does their laundry, and who takes them shopping for sneakers, and who gets out of bed at night when they have nightmares. I'm their mom.'

Michiko's husband, Yamato, blurts out, 'And I am the breadwinner in this family. I'm the one that pays for the food you cook, who bought the nice car you drive to that top notch private school, that I also pay for, not to mention the designer sneakers. I'm the guy that pays for the roof over your very head.' By the end, Yamato's face is beet red.

It's working. The scene's been set up well enough that Michiko's beginning to cringe from the sound of Yamato's voice. But I don't intervene. I want to see where this is going.

'Judge,' Michiko says, 'right now I have 32 private piano students whom I see every week. I earn enough money to take care of my own children. My children have already told you they want to live with me, that they don't want to move to Tokyo, that they don't want to leave their school, and that they don't want to live with their father.'

'And,' the judge says, 'I don't appreciate your telling me again. I am well aware of what your children want, but they are children and have no idea as to what is, in the long run, best for them. The decision is up to me, not up to them, and not up to you.'

'They have also told you they are terrified of their father,' Michiko adds, cowering.

'You liar! You total and complete liar,' Yamato yells, standing up and throwing his pen across the room, almost hitting Michiko in the face.

Terror. There it is, Michiko's eyes frozen in fear. She sits, glued to her chair, her body looking weak and hopeless.

I quietly enter, kneel down beside her, place my right hand softly over her shoulders and my left hand over her clenched hands that sit on her lap. 'Michiko, let's just freeze the frame here. Stay exactly as you are in your body and from the bottom up describe to me what you are sensing.'

Michiko says, 'I'm pulling my feet almost off the ground. My knees are touching, and I feel like I'm jamming my thighs back into my hip sockets. My stomach is tight. I'm not breathing. The middle of my back is pressing against the back of the chair. My hands hurt. My shoulder blades are hunched up toward my ears, and my head is pressed down between them.' 'Michiko, can you see the exact shape your whole body is taking, as if you were looking at a puppet?' 'Yes, I can see it,' Michiko says. 'Let me ask you, do you want to be like this?' 'No, I don't.' 'Good, you are now about a third of the way home.'

'Okay, Michiko. If you are the one holding yourself in this position, then you are the one who can let go of holding yourself in this position. Let's begin by letting your feet come back to the ground. What happens as you do that?' 'My legs come down and my knees begin to separate a little.' I place the hand that was over her hands onto her left knee and then over to her right knee, suggesting that her knees could release slightly away from her hip joints. I watch more air enter her lungs but say nothing about it. I quietly stand up behind Michiko, place my hands along the sides of her ribs, and ask her to let the entire surface of her back spread out against the back of the chair. I feel more air coming into her lungs. I reach around and gently place my index finger onto the top of her sternum and from there gently guide her head back on top of her spine. Her eyelids flutter for a few seconds, followed by two slow blinks. Her eyes appear to settle back into their eye sockets. She's calm.

'Okay, Michiko. Now you are two-thirds of the way home. This next part I can't help you with. Only you can do it. I want you to find out what would happen if you decided not to fight, not to flee, not to freeze, and not to fidget. Can you make the decision not to fight . . . not to flee . . . not to freeze . . . and not to fidget?' I wait and watch Michiko as she becomes deeply and quietly strong. 'Can you sense what happens when you make that decision?' 'Yes, I can.' 'Good. Now become that decision.'

I ask Yamato to continue.

Yamato looks at the judge and says. 'Judge, my wife is lying to you. She's a compulsive liar. That is what she does best. My kids don't hate me.' Yamato turns toward Michiko, glares at her and says, 'You wait. You just wait.'

Michiko's body remains strong and open, her face calm. She's breathing. Quietly Michiko stands up, looks at the judge, and says, 'Your Honour, I'd like to submit for your judgement the evidence just set before you. Thank you for considering it.'

The judge turns, looks at Yamato, then at Michiko, and says nothing. He appears to be reconsidering, re-evaluating the situation.

'Michiko,' I say. 'That is what it feels like when the master is home.'

'Let's take a twenty-minute break. Go out and get some fresh air, and then let's come back and think about that last bit of very good work.'

The teachers return. I wait until everyone is settled. I let my eyes travel around the room, seeing each face. I let myself sit in the silence for ten or fifteen seconds.

'Okay, class, what was Michiko's goal?'

Not to lose custody of her kids.

'That's right. That's what she told us.'

'You can't practise "the means-whereby" unless you've got an end. Our work is about ends and means, about how we are being as we move toward our end, whatever that end may be. The experiment is not to compromise the means for the end, not to sacrifice our integrity along the way, and then see what happens. That's our practice. That's why I don't like thinking about Alexander's work as a technique. I think of it as a practice because it's hard, and I for one fail a lot. And sometimes I don't. I'm making progress. It takes practice.'

'So let's see if we can find the means-whereby inside of what just happened. Where does it begin?'

You stopped everything.

'That's true, and what is also true is that in real life you can't stop a situation like that. You can't say, "Okay judge. This is getting too intense. Let's just take a pause here so I can calm down." Here is an idea I want you to understand. Alexandrian inhibition, that is, deep neurological stopping, does not necessarily happen just because you stop an action. It only happens when you succeed in stopping your habitual holding pattern within the action. So when I froze the frame, I only stopped the action. Stopping the action, freezing the frame, pushing the pause bottom is a teaching device allowing me to slow everything down. So, what happened after I froze the frame?'

You asked her what she was sensing.

'Right. Michiko shifts from being kinaesthetically unconscious to becoming kinaesthetically conscious, which means she can now begin to sense how she is doing what she is doing. Once Michiko knows what she's doing to herself, she has a chance of undoing it. As Marj Barstow used to tell us, "You have to know where you are before you can make a change." So because she knew where she was, and because Michiko has had a good bit of training, she could come out of this pattern with only a little guidance from me.

'I was being her messenger. Interestingly, in both Hebrew and Greek the word for messenger is also the word for angel. In a way I was being her guardian angel. Alexander called messages "directions". I think of messages as messages in a bottle that drift to the edge of the shore. You pick up the bottle, reach in, and read the message. My first message to Michiko was, "You are not alone", and then, "Michiko, become kinaesthetically aware of yourself", and then, "You're one-third of the way home", and then, "Do you want to be this way?", and so on. Messages were being communicated not only through my words, but through how I was in my own body and being, through the quality of my voice, and of course through the quality of my touch. I was sending her messages through her knees, and ribs, and sternum, and she made good use of them. And next?'

Well, as those messages got through to her I could see Michiko's primary movement emerging. As soon as her legs began to let go I could see her neck begin to free and her head poise returning, and I could see her whole body opening up and the air filling her lungs. She was coming into a kind of quiet power. But the most impressive change was in her face, how the fear fell away.

'Good. So far we have:

One: the goal, the end.
Two: the employment of freezing the frame, a pedagogical device.
Three: the awakening of kinaesthetic consciousness.
Four: her decision that she didn't want to be this way, her willingness to let go of how she was holding on to herself.

Five: the freeing and redirecting of the energy contained within her former holding pattern.

Six: that energy expressing itself as primary movement, restoring her physical and psychological integrity.

You may have noticed that four, five, and six blend together. They happen, as Alexander described, "Altogether, one after the other." And then?'

You asked her to make a decision not to fight or flee or freeze or fidget.

'Right. The moment she let go of any preparation or impulse to fight, flee, freeze, or fidget, was the moment of Alexandrian inhibition, the moment of deep neurological stopping. In that moment Michiko was free. The making of that decision, consciously, prepared Michiko for the critical moment, for that moment when she's going to want to go back to her old way of reacting to Yamato and to the judge. Michiko's decision is going to have to be incredibly deep. The critical moment is also the moment of opportunity, it's the moment in which she has the opportunity to remain free. Erika Whittaker said it this way: "Inhibition is decision". Alexandrian inhibition is sticking to your decision against your habit of life. It's not going back into some past pattern but going forward into a free future.

'So I'm watching to make sure Michiko is accessing tremendous inhibitory power within herself, and then I tell her, I send her a message, and that message is . . . ?'

To become that decision.

'Yes, because Alexandrian inhibition is not something we can do. It's only a way we can be. Her decision must be embodied if it is to work.'

'Seven: making it through the critical moment. And she did.

'And then what happened?'

Michiko responded to Yamato and to the judge the way she wanted.
'And what do we call that in the Alexander world?'
Choice?
'That's a good answer.'
Freedom.
'Another good answer.'
Constructive conscious control.
'Another good answer. Something tells me Alexander would have liked that answer.'

'When Michiko adhered to the means-whereby she didn't disintegrate. She could function without debilitating fear. She could say what she wanted to say the way she wanted to say it, without fighting, without withdrawing, and without panicking. She could think on her feet. She could take care of herself, and, to the best of her ability, her children.'

'Will she get custody of her children? Will she achieve her end? We don't know. But we do know she was her best self in that courtroom. We watched her find her integrity, her dignity. We can't entirely control how our lives unfold, nor the lives of our children. But with training we can learn to attend to our integrity.'

'And we can let our children see that.'

TALKING TO PEOPLE

1 THE LAY OF THE LAND

———◆·▪·◆———

In Japan people work late, often at jobs that have little to do with who they are. They finish work and desperately want to do something for themselves, something they care about. The scene in the Japanese version of *Shall We Dance*, when the woman rushes in late to her dance class, not having had time to eat, and faints on the spot from exhaustion, is not an exaggeration.

That's how it was for some of my night students. They'd arrive and there they were, not really standing but ever so slightly wavering in the air, on the verge of fainting, famished, weary, drained.

There was no other way to work with them but lying down. My friend Anchan had just made new teaching tables for the Alexander Alliance Japan. They were low, about a foot off the ground so that we could work in *seiza*. It was easier to work on these tables than to work on the floor. The tables were shaped vaguely like a person, which made sense. They were wider than a massage table at the upper end, providing plenty of room for the arms, while the middle was quite narrow, allowing the teacher to come in close to the student's torso, making it really easy to reach over to the other side, and the lower end of the table widened out slightly for the pelvis, legs, and feet. For me, it was perfect.

Our sessions were quiet, meditative, long, sometimes lasting for an hour. Strangely enough, rarely did a student fall asleep. Usually at some point, a student would begin to talk to me and to Midori Shinkai, who was serving as my translator, and we would listen.

There was little I gave in the way of reply. I replied with my hands, helping them to become soft within themselves as they spoke to us of their hardships.

Sometimes, I'd sit there feeling like an old tree providing shade and shelter. Sometimes, I'd become so utterly silent, it was as if I could hear the ocean inside of them. They would leave, rested and awake, as if they had suddenly remembered who they were and why they were alive.

That was years ago. I had fallen out of doing lying down work. I had moved on to other ways of working. For 40 years my work has led me to where it has wanted me to go, and I have followed like a faithful servant.

Yamashita-san arrives, an Alexander Technique teacher. He specifically requests a lying down lesson. 'I'm so sorry,' I say. 'I hardly ever do table work. It's not what I am trained in, not what I practise, not what I am good at.' '*Yoroshiku onegaishimasu,*' he says. 'Please teach me.' I tell him I will do my best for him.

'Okay. Let's begin.' We open up a standard massage table. 'Yamashita-san, without thinking, just lie down on the table any old way.' Like a high jumper he performs a kind of western roll onto the table, ending up on his back, legs outstretched and turned out, his head slightly tilted back, his hands resting on his belly. 'That's great. Don't move. Don't correct anything. Don't arrange yourself. Don't do the Alexander Technique. Just hang out and rest.

'This may not be the conventional way to begin an Alexander lying down lesson, but entertain me. I have my reasons, which I will share with you all along the way. I want you to understand my mind, then, if you ever want to, it will be easier for you to do what I do.

'You look comfortable. I like being comfortable too. No point being uncomfortable.' I pull up a fairly high stool. It is what happens to be in the studio. I place it at the end of the table, just behind Yamashita-san's head, and sit down.

'Okay, Yamashita-san. Here's the first thing I do. I look. I look at my student, my person, without any desire to come toward them and help them, without a desire to change them in any way. At the same time, I don't pull back away from them and begin critically analysing everything I see. It's as if I were far away, high on a mesa, gazing out over a vast, beautiful landscape. Yet, I feel strangely close to what I am seeing, almost touching it with my eyes while at the same time receding from it, as if I were on a ship leaving a place I love.

'Usually, when we see something, the first thing we do is to identify it. Our minds quickly name what we see. I look at you and my mind says "man". And then the mind thinks that it no longer has any more to do. Its job is finished. But years ago, when I first started birdwatching, I read a book written by Donald and Lillian Stokes on bird behaviour. They said that if you really want to go beyond identification, if you really wanted to see a bird, to see its behaviour, how it lives its life, you had to watch it at the very least for three minutes. After three minutes, and not until then, you begin seeing what is actually going on in front of your eyes, not the name, a red-winged blackbird, not the symbol, not the icon of a red-winged blackbird, but the life of a particular bird. You begin taking in the being-ness of the bird.

'So that's what I am going to do with you now, and I will share with you what I am seeing. This will begin to awaken your kinaesthetic sense, as you will soon experience. This is important, as you know. You probably also know that in the early 1900s Alexander published some writings on the re-education of kinaesthetic systems. So that's what we'll be doing for a little while.'

'Let's begin by looking at the lay of the land. To do that I imagine a strong rain raining down on a vast area of land, which is you. I watch where it looks like the rain would seep into the ground, where it would collect, and where it would begin to run down, and the path that watercourse would take.

'When the rain hits your sternum,' touching his sternum in the place I want him to sense, 'I see the rain running down toward your left shoulder/boulder, collecting, and then cascading down into the pit, the armpit.' I slide down his sternum, following the incline toward his left armpit. I return to the ridge of the sternum and slide my hand to the right, along land that Yamashita-san will likely notice is unlike his left side.

'What's happening kinaesthetically, Yamashita-san?' I say, noting he's wide awake. 'I can sense and see exactly what you are seeing,' he says. We continue in this way until Yamashita-san has a vivid sense of his body's landscape: the slope of his forehead, the arching Japanese Monet-like bridge under his neck, the caves under his hands and feet, the pools of his eyes, his rib cave-ity, the pelvic ravine, the roll of his legs.

'Now, having awakened your kinaesthesia, having got a sense of the lay of the land, I will begin to use my hands. If we extend this metaphor, my hands would play the part of external forces which change the shape of the earth: the sun, the wind, the rains, and time itself.'

As I work with my hands, I not only talk to Yamashita-san about what I am doing, I tell him why I am doing what I am doing, sometimes how I am doing what I am doing, and sometimes from whom I learned to do what I am doing. 'That's from Elisabeth Walker, that's indirectly from Joan Murray, that's from Robyn Avalon, that I made up, that too, that's from Robin Simmons, that's from Walter Carrington, that move is from Nica Gimeno, that's an image from Martha Hansen Fertman, that image is from Ethel Webb,* this idea is from Barbara Conable.'

Along the way I tell Yamashita-san why I don't work symmetrically, why I don't have a set routine, why I use myriad qualities of touch, why I work unpredictably, why I don't talk about breathing, how I get shoulders to widen and settle, wrists to unset, ribs to soften, nostrils to open, organs to move, hip joints to un-grip, legs to balance themselves.

The hour flies by, and yet it's as if we've traveled together for years, hiking up hills, rafting down rivers, climbing up cliffs, sliding down slopes, camping out in caves, resting upon rocks.

Who knows? Maybe I'll get back into table work again someday. Maybe not. It's not up to me. I'm a servant. I listen to my master.

---

* The image was one that Ethel used with Erika Whittaker, her niece, when Erika was eight years old. Ethel knew that Erika loved strawberry jam on her morning toast, so she would ask Erika to allow her back to spread out on the floor like strawberry jam on a piece of toast.[20]

2 NO SWEAT

A man walks in, muscular, not a lean and mean muscularity, but a firm, round, bear-like muscularity. He's the kind of man that would use his power to protect someone in need, rather than bully someone for the fun of it.

'What brings you here, Yasuo-san? Noriko-sensei tells me you are a physical therapist and in your spare time a parachute glider.'

I'm expecting Yasuo to begin talking about some physical issue. A painful, lonely sadness fills his eyes.

The three of us, Yasuo-san, Masako, who is translating for me, and I sit together for a good minute in silence, which is not uncommon after I ask someone a question in Japan. Japanese people rarely blurt out their first thought. It's as if they let the question sink down into some place full of unshared secrets.

'I want to relax,' Yasuo says.

'How do you know you are not relaxed?'

'I feel nervous.'

'What happens when you get nervous?'

'I begin to sweat. A lot. I feel embarrassed and ashamed that I am sweating.'

'When does this happen most?'

'When I am with people. When I have to talk to people.'

'Usually when we are with people we are with family, or roommates, or friends, or coworkers, or strangers. Do you have any family,' I ask?

'Not much. My parents live far away. I'm not married. I live alone.'

'Who are you with, and what situation are you in when this happens most intensely?'

'When I meet a stranger. When I have to talk to someone I don't know.'

'Does it happen more when the stranger is a woman or a man?'

'Definitely a woman.'

I can see a change in Yasuo's skin colour. He's becoming pale. The back of his skull has pulled back. I see an image of a horse and the rider pulling the reins back.

'Well, Masako is a woman, so why don't you have a conversation with Masako? You've never met her before. She's a stranger. Face each other and have a conversation.'

Yasuo's eyes open wide.

'Turn your chairs so you're facing one another. Get a little bit closer. There you go. That's perfect.'

Masako has played these kinds of roles for me in other lessons. She's a natural. Masako takes on a slightly shy demeanor, looks down, then looks up.

'How did you get such a strong body? Do you do some kind of sport?' Masako asks.

Yasuo mentions that he does parachute gliding and that the equipment is heavy so it requires a good bit of strength. Masako lights up a bit, crosses her legs and asks him to tell her more about it.

Yasuo takes out a handkerchief, something almost all men and women in Japan carry on them, and wipes his forehead, which is sweating profusely.

I've got Yasuo exactly where I want him.

'Okay, Yasuo-san. I see what you are doing that might be making you sweat. Of course, I don't know for sure. But the only way we can find out is if there is some way I can get you to stop doing what I see you doing. Does that make sense?'

'*Hai*,' Yasuo says. 'What do you see?' he asks.

'What I see is that you are very muscular. It is almost like you live in your muscular system, especially in your large action muscles, like your quads, and abs, and traps, and deltoids, and biceps, and pecs.

'When you get nervous and begin to sweat, I'm not sure if I am making this up, but I think I see your body swelling, as if your large action muscles all at once are becoming hypertonic, even though you are not moving. It's as if your body wants to move, but it's frozen and can't. You're sitting there trying to move and trying not to move at the same time, so your body is working out like mad, and you are breaking out in a sweat.'

'*Ah . . . so . . . kaa . . .* I see what you mean,' Yasuo says, wondering.

'Sometimes I get locked into my muscular system too. I've got a particular way of getting out of it. Want to learn it?'

'*Hai.*'

'I use my imagination, which is one way of using your mind. I imagine I have an outer body and an inner body. Actually, I do more than imagine it. I pretend, as a child would, that it is absolutely true, that my inner body exists. And I don't only imagine it, I sense it through my kinaesthetic sense. It's more like a "ki-mage". "Ki" in your language means mind, heart, spirit, feeling, energy, and that is exactly what a kimage is made of. So your inner body is not muscular or physical. It lives deeper within you than your muscular body. It lives under your entire muscular body. We think we have lots of different muscles in the body, but really it's more like we have one unified muscular system, just like we have one circulatory system. This muscular system is a bit like a cylindrical trampoline wrapped around your skeletal system. Deep within you, underneath your muscular system, you have an inner body totally unattached to your muscular body. I'd like you to imagine, to ki-magine that your muscular body is like an astronaut suit, but the real you is inside and not physical. Your astronaut suit is not you, but your inner body is. Your inner body is who you are, where you exist. Your inner body is your home, where you can rest, and from where you can move.

'So can you just sit where you are? Close your eyes and lean back against the chair. Get support from the chair. Slide your feet way out in front of you, so you can't push down with your feet against the floor. Can you let your belly un-tighten?'

I go over, place my hand on his chest until I feel my hand gently sink into him like smoke permeating a sweater.

'Drop below your astronaut suit, Yasuo-san,' I say. I touch the outside of his upper arms, always with this permeating quality, then around his skull, then along the sides of his body, along the sides of his pelvis, on his quadriceps, his calves, his feet. I watch his face. He is no longer sweating. His breathing is slower. He looks like he's about to fall asleep.

'Yasuo-san. When I ask you to, I want you to slowly open your eyes but, before you do, I want you to decide not to push out into your muscles. I want you to decide not to turn your muscles on. Keep your muscle-switch off. As your eyes open, if you feel your-self beginning to push into your muscles, just lower your eye-lids, turn your muscle-switch off, and return to your inner body. Calmly, but firmly, say to yourself "off . . . off . . . off . . . off", as you open your eyes, until your eyes are open and there you are, seeing and resting in your inner body. Then, when Masako begins talk-ing to you, I want you to say to yourself gently and firmly, "off . . . off . . . off . . ." until she is finished speaking. Okay?'

'Okay.'

Yasuo sits. I can see him dropping in below his muscles. He begins to open his eyes but decides to close them again. On the third go he opens them and keeps them open. He's completely resting in the chair and resting in himself. Masako asks him about his parents, where they live, and what they do. I see a slight push into his muscles, and then I see him drop back in.

'My parents live in Kanazawa, not far from Kenrokuen garden,' he says. I watch Yasuo finish speaking and then drop back into his inner body.

'How are you doing, Yasuo-san?'

'I can do it. I have control over it. It's like I found that switch in me, and when it goes on I can turn it off.'

'How does that make you feel?'

'It makes me feel soft and kind and happy.'

'And you are not sweating.'

'I'm not sweating.'

'Yes, inner bodies are not physical, so they don't sweat. They can't sweat.'

'Yasuo. We've been working about 35 minutes, and our lesson is supposed to be 45 minutes but I am going to stop here. You learned what you came here to learn. You found your inner body, and you found your on/off switch which controls your large action muscles and allows you to rest in your inner body. With a little practice you will be able to do this whenever you want. You know how to sit and rest in your inner body. You have this little meditation you can practise whenever you have time.'

'*Arigatou gosaimashita*,' I say, bowing. 'It was wonderful to work with you. I learned a lot from you,' I say, feeling myself at that moment living deep within my inner body, thinking how I am always teaching myself what I most need to learn, saying what I most need to hear.

3 THE WALKER

At Crosslands, a Quaker retirement community, 15 eager students, between the ages of 85 and 105, wait for the workshop to begin. After learning everyone's name and talking a bit about what will happen in the workshop, I ask them if there are any activities that are hard for them. All hands go up. One woman's sparkly eyes catch my attention. I begin with Agnes.

Sitting fairly upright, Agnes aligns her walker squarely in front of her chair, easily stands up, then very slowly shuffles over to me. The bottoms of her feet are not leaving the ground. Her ankles remain locked in a 90-degree flexion. Her knees hardly bend. Her hip joints look stiff. She's hunched over.

'Agnes, would you mind walking back to your chair, and sitting down again?' Thinking that a bit odd, she nonetheless turns around and heads back to her chair.

I watch her slow, careful shuffling. I watch her tentatively turn around, pause, then gracefully sit down. Her hips, knees, and ankles all flex smoothly and easily. Her balance is good. She's transferring very little weight into her walker. I ask her to lean back against the back of the chair and just get comfortable. Her spine naturally lengthens. Her poise is good. I'm wondering . . .

'Agnes, did you ever fall when you were walking?' 'Yes I did, and I broke my hip.' 'When was that?' I ask. Agnes calculates. 'Nine years ago.'

'Agnes, I couldn't help noticing how naturally upright you are when you are sitting, and how well your legs work when you stand up and when you sit down. You look really beautiful and strong. When you stand up and sit down your balance is so steady.' 'Really?' she says. 'Group, what did you see?' They agree. I can see they like Agnes.

'If I helped you with your walking, and if I promise you that you will not fall down or get hurt, would you consider working with me a little?'

Agnes thinks about it for a moment, smiles, and says, 'Sure.' She gets up and slowly shuffles over to me.

'Agnes, can you keep the same amount of pressure between your hands and the walker, but gently let your head float up a tiny bit further away from the walker, so your spine feels more like it does when you are sitting?' She becomes slightly more upright. Her eyes tell me she's a little scared. 'Agnes, you are safe. I promise. Tell me, do you feel more pressure or less pressure between your hands and the walker now?'

Surprised, she says, 'More.' 'Isn't that interesting? Your head's further away from the walker and somehow that allows you to transfer more of your weight through the walker into the ground. You are higher up and yet you're more stable. Can you feel that, Agnes? It's like this. A tall skyscraper could be very stable. And a little round hut close to the ground could be very unstable.' I can see the wheels spinning. She gets it. 'Are you trying to tell me that rounding over and trying to be closer to the ground might not be helping me?' she asks. 'Yep,' I say.

'Okay, Agnes, as you are standing there and sensing your stability, can you shift your weight slightly side to side, from your left foot, then to your right foot, and then back to your left foot, without losing your large, stable structure?' I can see that scares her a little so I walk around behind her, softly touch her ribs, almost surrounding them with my large, warm hands, and send a little support up through her spine. I see her collapsed chest fill out and her head come back over her neck. For assurance, I keep my hands on her ribs. Agnes shifts her weight. No problem. Then she shifts back again. No problem. I remove my hands so softly she doesn't realize they're not there. She shifts again. She continues several more times because she likes how it feels.

'Agnes. Well done. Now this time, when I finish talking, I want you to make sure that when you shift your weight, you shift your weight onto a truly straight leg, a completely straight leg. See what happens if you refuse to crouch over or bend your knees. But for this to work you are going to have to make up your mind to leave yourself up here, no matter how odd it feels. Go ahead and make your decision,' I say. I can see a brave look come onto her face. There's strength in her stance. 'Agnes, stick to your decision, and when you are ready, shift your weight.'

She does it perfectly. I see her friends in the class watching closely. No one is drifting off. 'Agnes, well done. This time, when you shift your weight to the left, as you did so well, be there for a second and bring your right knee forward and touch my hand.' My hand is now two inches in front of her knee. She does it and I say, 'Good.' I move my hand three inches away and ask her to touch my hand again and she does. Then four. Agnes looks really surprised. 'Agnes, that is what your knee does every time you sit down and get up, so I knew you could do that. I will not ask you to do anything that I don't know you can do. I promise.'

We do it to the other side. Occasionally I remind her, both verbally and tactually, of her long spine and of the better stability she has through the walker, and of her straight legs. She's now comfortable with my touch, which I use sparingly to remind her that she doesn't need to crouch down.

'Agnes, in a moment you are going to shift your weight to the left onto a straight leg, send your right knee more forward than usual, and when your knee is forward I want you to let your foot hang down like a horse's hoof. Then you are going to let your foot come down to the ground wherever it wants to.' She does it. No shuffling, no shuffling sound, but I do not say anything about it.

'Well done, Agnes. Is this fun?' Eyes sparkling, she says, 'Yes, fun.' 'Good. For me too.'

'Okay Agnes, can you sense that your feet are now slightly apart but instead of being side by side, one foot is just a little bit in front of the other?' She nods. 'Can you continue sensing all your stability, and shift your weight diagonally forward onto your straight right leg?' I am standing behind her, my hands on either side of her ribs, encouraging her to remain easily upright. She takes her step. 'Perfect.'

About ten minutes have gone by. We are in another world, a world where time has stopped. Agnes has taken one real step.

'Okay, Agnes. If you can take one step like that, one stable, safe step, then don't you think you could take two, and if you can take two safe, stable steps, don't you think you could take three? Agnes, decide to walk like that, at whatever speed feels comfortable for you. Go take your walker for a walk as if you were walking a shopping cart down the aisle of a supermarket.'

I stand behind her, placing my hands lightly upon the back and sides of her lower ribs. We're in tandem. When her right knee goes forward my right knee goes forward right under hers. But my touch is so light she hardly feels I am there. After taking about ten steps my touch fades away, unnoticed. She is walking on her own, with her walker; upright, stable, safe.

'Agnes. Look at George, and walk over to him.' She does. She's smiling. 'Now, look at Ethel and walk over to her.' She does. She's gaining confidence. 'Now, look at Ada and walk over to her.' She lets out a laugh. Each time she walks over to a person, Agnes is thinking less about herself and more about the person she is seeing. And each time, without noticing it, she is walking faster. Looking around I see, however, that Agnes's friends are noticing it.

I am standing in front of Agnes. I kindly hold my hands in front of her, inviting her to put her hands on top of mine. It's like I am inviting her to dance with me. Agnes looks me in the eyes, not thinking about her body, and places her palms on top of my palms. 'Agnes, I am going to ask George to move your walker because right now you don't need it, because I am going to be your walker, and I am a good walker.' George almost springs out of his chair and slides the walker out from between us. 'Agnes, I promise I will give you back your walker, but right now take me for a walk.' As Agnes walks forward, I walk backwards. She's leading and I am following. We're dancing.

'Agnes, walk me back to your chair.' She does. I sit down. My hands slide out from under Agnes's hands. Agnes is standing fully upright on her own, but I say nothing. I slide my hands back under Agnes's hand. I slowly begin to stand up and reflexively Agnes helps me onto my feet. I ask her to turn me around so we can switch places, because it is her turn to sit down. She is not thinking about herself, she is thinking about turning me around. She is in the lead.

'Thanks, Agnes. You can sit down now.' I drop my hands away and, without her walker, Agnes sits down.

Agnes feels safe, secure, and stable, because she is.

Postscript

When I taught at Crosslands Retirement Community I was just shy of 30. I had been teaching Alexander's work for five years. I had done well with Agnes but I was not so happy with the workshop as a whole. As I put on my coat, head down, feeling unsure of myself, an elderly man approaches, upright, tweed sports jacket and bow tie. There's a soft elegance about him.

He extends his hand and says, 'James, James Bennett. You might like knowing that 55 years ago I received lessons from Mr. Alexander. He used to tell me that, next to John Dewey, I was his worst student. I always took that as a compliment.'

'Well,' I said, taken aback, 'tell me, be honest, how did I do?' 'It moved me seeing you work with my friend Agnes,' he said. 'To see her walking without her walker was thrilling. You know, I had many lessons with F. M., but they were always individual lessons. I never watched anyone having a lesson. Until now I could never see what was actually happening. As for how you did? Have no doubt. You did splendidly. You have that touch.'

That made my day. Actually, that kept me going for years. It affirmed my intuition that Alexander's work could effectively be taught in groups. It further convinced me of the importance of being able to see Alexander's work, as subtle as it was. And I felt encouraged to keep cultivating 'that touch'. Early on I had made a vow to myself that I would not quit until my hands were as good as Marjorie Barstow's hands.

Forty years after having made that vow, a thousand workshops later, fifteen thousand people-under-my-hands later, I may have made it. I may have gotten there. I may have fulfilled my vow. I will never know for certain, because I will never know what my hands feel like to others, so best not to stop practising. I don't think I could stop practising. It's who I am, at my best.

TOUCHING PEOPLE

1 SEEK AND THOU SHALT NOT FIND

There's a time to seek and a time to sense.

Have you ever started looking for your glasses and then suddenly discovered they are resting on your nose? Or have you ever begun looking for your hat and then realized it's sitting on top of your head? That's what I mean.

There I am on my knees, doing my best to get the tip of my screwdriver into the groove of a tiny screw. I'm cranking my neck into some ungodly position, trying unsuccessfully to get my head in a place where I can see that screw, which is there, somewhere, in some dark, dusty corner inside some small kitchen cabinet. My friend, an experienced carpenter and Alexander teacher, says, 'Bruce, what would happen if you stopped trying to see that screw?' Immediately my entire body unwinds like a snake uncoiling, the head of the screwdriver drops into its groove, and the screwdriver begins turning as if by itself.

A woman, now living with and taking care of her aging mom, is trying to figure out how to get the lid of her mom's pressure cooker to snap into place. It's not happening. She tries harder, which means dropping her head down closer to the pressure cooker in an attempt to peer under and around the lid's rim. She hasn't breathed for about a minute, which is why, when she finally stops trying and gives up, I hear a huge inhale and then a huge exhale accompanied by an exasperated collapse of her chest. 'Okay, Renate, how about we let go of that pressure cooker because the only pressure I can see cooking is in you and not in that pot. Let me ask you, are you having any success seeing what you are looking for?' 'No, I am not,' she says with a big smile on her face, a sign of recognition and understanding.

Thinking of my dear friend, carpenter, and Alexander colleague, Rob Gepner-Muller, I say, 'Renate, back away from the stove and get a bit of distance between you and the pressure cooker. That's good. Now just stand where you are.' I go over to her and gently help re-establish an easy but strong internal alignment, engage some core support, a bit of ground connection, encourage breathing. 'Okay, Renate, we know that looking for what you cannot see doesn't work, so go over and give it another go.' Renate walks over, her left hand taking hold of the handle of the pot, her right hand the handle of the lid, and begins trying to see what's under the lid. I sneak up on her, silently place one of my hands on the back of her head and the other over her hands, so that she won't try to straighten up and correct herself, and ask her to stay exactly where she is. Again, another big smile. 'I'm looking for what I can't see,' Renate says. 'Renate, give up seeing. Close your eyes. Be blind. Her eyelids lower, her shoulders drop and spread, air fills her lungs, the lid drops and snaps into place, her hands turn, she opens her eyes, which are now sparkling, and lets out a big laugh. Everyone is amazed. Me too.

Two speech therapists are working together. They want me to watch a particular technique that's difficult for them. I watch as this sensitive young man palpates somewhere under his patient's chin, for what I am not sure. Maybe her tongue, maybe not. I decide not to ask for the details. I don't want to get too involved, which of course I really do want to do because I want to learn about everything. But I know from experience that it is often better for me to stay out of my student's business, out of the content of the activity, and simply watch as a naive observer. Wise innocence. I see him peeking under his patient's chin, looking for something. Then he takes a tissue and asks his patient to open her mouth and gently stick out her tongue. With the tissue he lightly holds the extended tip of her tongue in what I am guessing is an attempt to get the tongue to relax and widen. Now, he's craning his neck to look down her throat.

'Hiroki-san, I don't know what you are trying to do, and I don't know what you are trying to see. But what I do know is that you are trying real hard to see something. And my experience tells me that sometimes, if we stop trying to see something that may be too hard for us to see, our other senses will take on the job that the eyes just can't do. Other senses step up and figure it out. So see what happens if you gently lower your eyelids the way you do when you smell a flower you are holding under your nose, and just continue to do your work.'

As he smells the imaginary flower under his nose, immediately his head poise establishes itself. A beautiful sense of space surrounds him. He's looking like a great orchestra conductor. I don't know why. His fingers look like they are doing the seeing now. His tactile sense has taken over.

'*Do desuka?* What's happening?' I ask, one of my favourite questions. 'I'm getting what I want,' he says. 'Great. *Sugoi,*' I say. 'And how about you?' I ask, turning to the patient. The patient, actually another speech therapist, says that his touch changed completely, that at first it was pokey and a little uncomfortable for her, and that now his fingers are so soft she doesn't even feel them. 'All I feel is what is happening inside my mouth, inside my own body,' she says.

There's a time to seek and a time to sense.

2 TOUCHING IMPERMANENCE

I didn't know her. Mollie, one of my students, asked me if I would work with her, with her friend who was dying, and without thinking I said, 'Sure, sure I'll work with her.'

Driving over to her house, to Sharon's house, that familiar feeling descended upon me, enveloping me like some thick fog in the night, this feeling of being lost, of wondering what I was going to do when I met Sharon, of not knowing how I could possibly help her.

It took Sharon a long time to get to the front door. She managed a small, heartfelt smile and invited me in. There was a massage table set up in the living room. Sharon said that Mollie thought I might need it. 'How about we get started?' I said, feeling nervous. 'Just take off your shoes and lie down on the table, on your back.' This too took a long time. I watched. Sharon was 40 but she moved as if she were 90. Why was no one with her? Why was she alone?

I helped Sharon to sit on the table, then, cradling her in my arms, I lowered her gently down into a semi-supine position. I pulled up a dining room chair and placed it at one end of the table, by her head. I sat down. 'Sharon, I'm just going to sit here for a while and be with you, and look at you. Is that okay?' She nodded.

I began surveying her thin, scared body. I wasn't looking for anything. I was just looking. Nothing was presenting itself. A wave of self-doubt washed over me and then all at once, as though my eyes had grown accustomed to the dark, I could see. I could see her.

Her right hand in a fist, her wrist curled inward. Her left arm pulled against her side. Shoulder blades drawn up toward her head, head pressed down into her neck, chest caved in, pelvis tucked under, like a dog with its tail between its legs. Thighs tight, pressed together. Brow knitted, eyes pressed shut, jaw clenched.

'What was that pattern?', I asked myself. Then it hit me. Sharon was bracing for impact, as if she was about to be in a head-on collision.

'Okay, Sharon, I'm seeing you. Tell me, what do you want?' 'I want to die,' she says. 'I'm trying to die.'

No one had ever said that to me. I felt my heart drop. 'Okay,' I said. 'I can see how you are holding on, how you are bracing. Maybe you want to die and your body doesn't. Maybe your body's scared of dying.'

'That's it,' Sharon says. 'I'm ready but my body isn't. Can you help me?' Sharon asks. 'I can teach you how to let go of your body. That's good for people when they are alive, and you are still alive. It might help you live until you die.' 'Okay,' she says.

Something tells me to begin with the large flexor muscles in Sharon's body, her quadriceps and her biceps. With the lightest touch a lot of tension immediately falls away. Her pelvis releases. Her right fist un-clutches. Her lungs fill with air. 'Are you okay, Sharon?' Sharon nods and I notice that her knitted brow has begun to relax.

Her feet. Her right foot is sickled inward, twisted inward, much the way her right hand was. I return to my chair and look again. Her body is rising and falling. She's moving. I place my hands around her head. 'Sharon, imagine your head is a large ostrich egg and my hands are a warm nest. Immediately I sense her neck muscles let go. I see her foot un-sickle, her arms relax away from her sides. Her chest is no longer caved in, but filled out and moving. Her jaw has unclenched and her lips are now ever so slightly parted, like a baby.

I spend the next half hour touching impermanence, finding soothing images Sharon can connect with that help her to let go whenever her body begins to tighten up on her . . . the scapulae as rafts gently drifting apart on the surface of a quiet lake . . . the sun setting between her eyes . . . the body as nothing but empty sky.

It's time to go. Sharon gives me a hug by the door. Her body feels soft, unafraid. We say our goodbyes.

Five days later Sharon died.

3 GOD IN THE PALM

OF YOUR HAND

Theology to me is not spiritual; it's tangible. It's earthy. It's physical. It's tactual.

Carl Jung writes, 'God is reality itself.' For me, reality feels pretty physical. You know, getting up, bathing, grooming, eating and going to work, or going to look for work. Or on other days, cleaning your house, going shopping for food, taking your car, if you have one, into the shop for an oil and filter change.

And then, on occasion, there's a free day. You're out in the country. A cool breeze brushes against your face. The warmth of the sun sits on your shoulders. You hear the sound of a stream nearby, smell a slight scent of cedar in the air.

Perhaps it makes sense to think about a theology of touch.

No one knows the story behind Michelangelo's choice. What we do know is that in the Torah God blew the breath of life through Adam's nostrils. Breath was the vital force.

Yet, when painting the Sistine Chapel Michelangelo chose not to depict the creation of Adam through this image. He chose touch, not breath. God touches Adam, and Adam lives. That's closer to how it works. Two people embrace. Spermatozoa contact the ovum. At seven-and-a-half weeks a fetus senses itself being touched and remains touched and touching, continually, until birth. If deprived of touch, infants die.

When my wife and I adopted Noah, our second baby from Korea, Noah was gaunt and withdrawn. His digestion was not good. He didn't eat much. He was uncomfortable. He rarely smiled. It didn't matter. We loved him infinitely anyway.

Our babies arrived on Korean time so when we were ready to go to sleep, they were just waking up for the day. Being the light sleeper in the house, I was the one who stayed up at night with the babies. One night while feeding Noah from a bottle, I noticed how his shoulder blades were acutely drawn together and tightly pulled up toward the back of his head, almost always a sign of fear or anxiety. In Noah it felt like fear.

After feeding Noah I'd sit down on the floor, lean my back against the wall and with my knees up, I'd place Noah's little back against my thighs so he could lean back as well and face me. I became the perfect reclining chair for Noah. I'd reach around to his back, placing each of my hands on a tiny shoulder blade. I just relaxed and rested my hands, rested my entire body, and dropped into a deep calmness within myself. I imagined my hands, and with them Noah's shoulder blades, sliding down away from the back of his head and around toward the sides of his little ribs.

A week went by and it seemed there was no way Noah was going to let those shoulder blades go. But he was my son, and I was not about to give up. One night all at once, like a little avalanche, Noah's shoulder blades completely released and spread wide apart. A big smile spread across his whole face. He threw his head back and let out a huge laugh. The next morning he had a big appetite, his digestion returned to normal, he had twice the energy and began gaining weight.

God in the palm of your hand.

JAPANESE WORDS AND PHRASES

arigatou gosaimashita (polite): Thank you.

chawan – a bowl for preparing and drinking tea.

choto mata kudasai: Please wait a bit / Pause.

do desuka: What is happening? / What is going on?

doumo (informal): Thank you / Hello / Goodbye

doumo arigatou gosaimashita: Thank you very much.

douzo: Begin / By all means / Please.

hai: Yes / I agree with you / Correct / I am ready.

hashi – chopsticks.

hiragana – is a phonetic syllabrary system comprised of 46 symbols, one of three Japanese writing systems.

kotatsu – a low, wooden table frame covered by a futon, or heavy blanket, upon which a table top sits.

ohayo gosaimasu: Good morning.

omatase (*shimashita*): I'm sorry to have kept you waiting / Thanks for waiting.

onegaishimasu (short version of *yoroshiku onegaishimasu*): Please help me / Please teach me / Please work with me.

otsukaresama deshita: Good job, we deserve to be tired.

seiza – A traditional and formal way of sitting, kneeling on the floor, folding one's legs underneath one's thighs, while resting the buttocks on the heels.

shakuhachi – a traditional bamboo flute.

sugoi: Great / Amazing / Wow.

yoroshiku onegaishimasu: Please help me / Please take care of me.

yoi otoshi wo: Happy New Year.

wakarimasen: I've no idea / I don't understand.

zen zen chigau: Totally different.

REFERENCES

1. F. M. Alexander, *Aphorisms* (London: Mouritz, 2000) p. 88.
2. Aldo Leopold, *The Land Ethic. A Sand County Almanac* (New York: Oxford UP, 1949), pp. 224-225.
3. Sir Laurens van der Post, 'Our Mother Which Art in Earth' in *Quadrant: The Journal of Contemporary Jungian Thought* (New York: C.G. Jung Foundation, 1990) Volume 23, Number 2, pp. 9-19.
4. Theodor Schwenk, *Sensitive Chaos: The Creation of Flowing Forms in Water and Air* (Rudolf Steiner Press, 2008) p. 25.
5. Friederich Novalis, *Aphorisms.* Quoted in Theodor Schwenk, *Sensitive Chaos*, p. 58.
6. F. M. Alexander 'Aphorisms', in *Articles and Lectures* (London: Mouritz, 2011), p. 193.
7. Aldo Leopold, *The Land Ethic. A Sand County Almanac* (New York: Oxford UP, 1949), pp. 224-225.
8. *Friedrich Nietzsche, Philosophical Writings,* edited by Reinhold Grimm (London: Continuum International Publishing Group, 1997), p. 242.
9. William Blake, *The Marriage of Heaven and Hell* (Boston: John W. Luce Company, 1906), p. 10.
10. Jacques Lusseyran, *And There Was Light* (California: New World Library, 2014), pp. 20-21.
11. *The Soul of Rumi,* annotated by Coleman Barks (New York: HarperCollins, 2002).
12. Meister Eckhart, *Selected Writings,* selected and translated by Oliver Davies (London: Penguin Classics, 1994), pp. 6-7.
13. F. M. Alexander 'Aphorisms', in *Articles and Lectures* (London: Mouritz, 2011), p. 186.
14. Rabbi Abraham Joshua Heschel, *Who Is Man?* (California: Stanford University Press, 1965), p. 45.
15. Elie Wiesel, Foreword to *The Nazi Doctors and the Nuremberg Code: Human Rights in Human Experimentation* edited by George J. Annas, Michael A. Grodin (New York: Oxford UP, 1995), p. ix.
16. 'What A Wonderful World', lyrics written by George Douglas, Bob Thiele and George David Weiss.

17. F. M. Alexander 'Aphorisms', in *Articles and Lectures* (London: Mouritz, 2011), p. 200.
18. Carl Rogers, *A Way Of Being* (Houghton Mifflin Company, 1980), p. 22.
19. Paul Éluard, https://en.wikiquote.org/wiki/Paul_%C3%89luard.
20. https://peacefulbodyschool.com/?s=conversations.

LIST OF ILLUSTRATIONS

Figure
1. Bruce Fertman with Tsutomu Nakano, Osaka, Japan, 2009.
2. 'Bulldogging' by permission of © Sue Niven 2017.
3. Delphic Sybil, Sistine Chapel, by Michelangelo Buonarroti (1475-1564), c. 1510, https://commons.wikimedia.org/wiki/Michelangelo.
4. Cumaean Sibyl, Sistine Chapel Ceiling, by Michelangelo Buonarroti (1475-1564), c. 1510. Copyright permission by © Bridgeman Images. Image number: AII344398.
5. Libyan Sybil, Sistine Chapel, by Michelangelo Buonarroti (1475-1564), c. 1510. Copyright permission by © Bridgeman Images. Image number: ELC847668.
6. Ignudo (detail), Sistine Chapel Ceiling, by Michelangelo Buonarroti (1475-1564), c. 1510. https://commons.wikimedia.org/wiki/Michelangelo.
7. Study for the Libyan Sybil, by Michelangelo Buonarroti, c. 1508. https://www.wikiart.org/en/michelangelo/study-to-the-libyan-sibyl.
8. Ignudo, Sistine Chapel Ceiling, by Michelangelo Buonarroti (1475-1564), c. 1510. https://commons.wikimedia.org/wiki/Michelangelo.
9. Plate from *Albinus on Anatomy* (Dover, 1989) by Bernhard Siegfried Albinus, and edited by Robert Beverly Hale and Terence Coyle. Page 39 (detail).

27. 'Extasis de Santa Teresa' by Gian Lorenzo Bernini 1647–52, Santa Maria della Vittoria, Rome. Photo: Bruce Fertman.
28. Saint Catherine of Siena near Castel Sant'Angelo, Rome, by Francesco Messina (1900-1995). Italy. Photo: Bruce Fertman.
29. 'Abundance' statue, Trevi Fountain, Rome, Italy. Photo: Bruce Fertman.
30. Bruce Fertman with member of Jeong Ga Ak Hoe, traditional Korean music ensemble, Seoul, Korea. Photo: Jeong Ga Ak Hoe.
31. Plate from *Albinus on Anatomy* (Dover, 1989) by Bernhard Siegfried Albinus, and edited by Robert Beverly Hale and Terence Coyle.
32. Bruce Fertman, Center for Integral Education for Artists, South Korea, 2016. Photo: Jeong Ga Ak Hoe.
33. Bruce Fertman, Seoul, South Korea, 2015. Photo: Shin Na Young.
34. Bruce Fertman with Sooyeon Kim, co-director of the Alexander Technique International School of Korea. Photo: Kay Kim.
35. Bruce Fertman teaching. Photo: Tada "Anchan" Akihiro.

ACKNOWLEDGEMENTS

Thanks goes to Jean Fischer for his formidable editing skills, for his patience and care. A thank you to John Tuite, Hendrik Klein and Jill Banwell for their taking the time to read my writings, for their astute feedback, and steadfast encouragement. A heartfelt bow to Tada Anchan Akihiro for his ability to see and capture people's inner beauty as it reveals itself through Alexander's work, and for being my photography coach. And to the members of Jeong Ga Ak Hoe for their photos of me teaching. I need not give thanks here to my teachers. I thank them every day. Lastly, I give thanks to all the people who have put their trust in me, who have placed themselves under my hands, who have shared their lives with me, who have touched me, changed me, brought out the best in me.

Bruce Fertman

INDEX